Reinhold Plastics Applications Series

No matter how remarkable the properties of a plastic may be, it is, after all, the most effective application of a material that counts. Many factors are involved in the determination of the optimum plastics application. If, for instance, a certain plastic answers all the physical requirements for a particular end use, it still may not be the material to select for such use if another material equal in properties is available at a lower price. The most obvious properties of a material do not always determine its best application. Such minor characteristics as workability and processing odors may need to be taken into account in their effect on operating conditions, and certain intangibles such as color and feel may have an effect on consumer acceptance.

Realizing the importance of correct application in the whole gamut of plastics activity, the Reinhold Publishing Corporation in 1956 decided to publish a series of short books emphasizing the applications of the various types of commercial materials of the plastics industry—each book to cover one type of material. The present volume by Bernard A. Dombrow is the second in this series. The first volume, "Polyethylene," by Theodore O. Kresser was published in July, 1957. Others now in process will cover acrylics, cellulosics, epoxies, fluorocarbons, gum plastics, ion exchange resins, laminates, polyamides, polyesters, polystyrenes, silicones, vinyls, and vacuum forming of plastics sheets.

The series is semi-technical—that is, one does not need to be a chemist to understand the various volumes. The authors have kept in mind as probable readers such industrial men and women as: design engineers, equipment manufacturers, producers of packages, manufacturers of machinery, students at technical schools and, of course, people more directly in the plastics industry—material manufacturers, molders, extruders, fabricators.

In addition to the above, it is hoped that each title will appeal to readers in specialized categories. Plastics from which fibers are made may be of interest to tire and fabric manufacturers. A book such as the one on vinyls, which materials are favorable for production of sheets, may have value for manufacturers of handbags and luggage. Similarly, other titles may appeal to manufacturers of paints, recorder tapes, upholstery, plywood, and furniture.

With this program in prospect it is with enthusiasm that this second book is presented.

HERBERT R. SIMONDS, *Editor*

Titles in Preparation

Acrylic Resins, *Nathaniel C. Ratner*

Cellulosics, *Walter Paist*

Epoxy Resins, *Irving Skeist*

Fluorocarbons, *Merritt A. Rudner*

Gum Plastics, *M. Stafford Thompson*

Laminates, *Charles Nerzig*

Plastic Sheet Forming, *Robert L. Butzko*

Polyamides, *Donald E. Floyd*

Polystyrene, *Harold M. Hartong*

Silicones, *F. M. Lewis and R. N. Meals*

Vinyls, *W. Mayo Smith*

Welding of Plastics, *F. J. Bockhoff and J. A. Neumann*

PREFACE

The purpose of this book is to present a broad panorama of the vast field of polyurethanes without going into too many technical details; it seeks to demonstrate general principles so that one not too versed in chemistry can obtain an understanding of the versatility and potential of this young plastic.

The author has addressed this volume to four groups of industrial personnel. The first group comprises those interested in the plastics industry but with little formal technical training. These, as well as those of the second group—technically trained non-chemists—may find it best to regard the polyurethanes merely as physical entities and to consider the chemistry involved only as a means of producing certain lines and linkages which result in materials having highly desirable physical properties. As these two groups need not spend much time on the chemistry involved, it has been presented as simply as possible. The third group includes those chemists who wish to make a general study of the field. The last group comprises those workers in one section of polyurethanes who wish to know something of other sections. It is hoped that these four groups can find enough detail for their immediate purposes in this book. As this book is not addressed primarily to a technical group, no attempt is made to give complete references. For those who wish more information, a bibliography of selected articles and patents is included.

The author wishes to thank the various companies in the

field, especially the producers of diisocyanates, for their assistance as may be noted by the various accredited illustrations and information. Credits to others are given whenever possible, with the hope that we have not overlooked anyone. I wish to extend my heartfelt thanks to the officers of the Nopco Chemical Company, especially those of the Plastics Division, for their aid, encouragement and permission to use data and illustrations. The author feels particularly indebted to the library of this company for its help in obtaining necessary reference material.

October 1957   BERNARD A. DOMBROW
North Arlington, N. J.

CONTENTS

Chapter   *page*

     PREFACE vii

1. INTRODUCTION 1

2. CHEMISTRY 11

3. RIGID FOAMS 29

4. SEMI-RIGID FOAMS 55

5. FLEXIBLE FOAMS 75

6. RUBBERS 106

7. ADHESIVES 124

8. COATINGS 134

9. TEXTILE APPLICATIONS 147

10. MISCELLANEOUS 157

11. HANDLING OF DIISOCYANATES 163

     BIBLIOGRAPHY 167

     APPENDIX 171

     INDEX 173

1. INTRODUCTION

The term "polyurethanes" refers to a new class of polymers that has found widespread commercial applications within the last twenty years. These materials represent the first industrially important and commercially useful culmination of an old line of organic research (namely, isocyanates) that started about one hundred years ago. A polyurethane is a polymer in which the repeating unit is a urethane linkage. However, the chemical term "urethane" is devoid of meaning to many workers in the plastics field; in fact, it characterizes a class of organic compounds which is usually not familiar to most chemists. Some chemists may recognize that urethanes are employed as derivatives in analytical chemistry to verify hydroxyl compounds by melting point determinations. A few may know of the use of ethyl urethane in medicine.

To understand this class of compounds, one must go back to the basic chemistry of carbonic acid and urea. In the classical preparation by Wöhler (1828) where, for the first time, an inorganic chemical was transformed into an organic chemical without the intervention of the so-called "vital force," heat converted ammonium carbonate to urea through the removal of water. Here, the intermediate compound is ammonium carbamate. Schematically, this may be shown as follows:

$$
\underset{\substack{\text{Ammonium}\\\text{carbonate}}}{\overset{\displaystyle \text{ONH}_4}{\underset{\displaystyle \text{ONH}_4}{\text{C}=\text{O}}}} \longrightarrow \underset{\substack{\text{Ammonium}\\\text{carbamate}}}{\overset{\displaystyle \text{NH}_2}{\underset{\displaystyle \text{ONH}_4}{\text{C}=\text{O}}}} \longrightarrow \underset{\substack{\textit{Urea}}}{\overset{\displaystyle \text{NH}_2}{\underset{\displaystyle \text{NH}_2}{\text{C}=\text{O}}}}
$$

Just as carbonic acid is only stable when it is combined in the form of either its salts or esters, so is the free carbamic acid. The latter decomposes quickly into ammonia and carbon dioxide. The only stable member of this series is urea, which is the complete diamide of carbonic acid. Because of this marked instability, carbamic acids exist in organic chemistry only in the form of their esters; these are called "urethanes," and may be characterized best by the following grouping:

$$
\overset{\displaystyle \text{OR}}{\underset{\displaystyle \text{N}\langle}{\text{C}=\text{O}}}
$$

which represents a generalized amide-ester of carbonic acid. The best known of these is ethyl urethane, usually called simply urethane ($NH_2COOC_2H_5$). It should be noted that at least three types of urethane are possible, depending upon whether substituent groups on the nitrogen atom are represented by two, one, or no hydrogens.

In order to understand how polymeric materials can be derived from these urethane linkages and made available for commercial exploitation, we will examine the physical build-up of the various polymers, ignoring, for the present, the various preparatory methods. If we take the urethane group, and, instead of using a simple alcohol to form the ester link, we utilize a polyhydroxyl material like glycol, etc., a point of growth is produced. Similar use of the proper polyfunctional nitrogen compounds in the preparations will supply other growth points at the amide linkage. The simplest form of polyurethane is the linear one, which may be represented in its most elementary form by the following:

$$-O-R_2-O-\underset{\underset{O}{\|}}{C}-\underset{\underset{H}{|}}{N}-R_1-\underset{\underset{H}{|}}{N}-\underset{\underset{O}{\|}}{C}-O-R_2-O-\underset{\underset{O}{\|}}{C}-\underset{\underset{H}{|}}{N}-R_1-\underset{\underset{H}{|}}{N}-\underset{\underset{O}{\|}}{C}-O-$$

where the urethane linkage is underlined. A chain of this nature would be comparable to nylon and other linear polymers, and this fact foretells its potential uses: material made thus as linear polyurethanes has applications in the form of fibers and bristles.

By incorporating higher functional materials, other than dibasic ones, polymers can be produced with various degrees of cross-linking, ranging from a few to many branches. Hence they give rise to synthetics which, in physical properties, vary from soft elastomers to rigid (even brittle) thermosetting plastics similar to phenolics. By merely varying the number of branchings, it is theoretically possible to produce plastics of physical characteristics duplicating any type of known plastic, from thermoplastic to thermosetting. In addition, it is possible to superimpose upon this variation those made possible by juggling the organic chemical groups present between the urethane groups. This would lead to even finer graduations in the physical properties.

Thus, for example, it is theoretically feasible to obtain a continuous spectrum of rigidity by these combinations and branchings. The number of possibilities is tremendous; in fact, one's imagination is staggered when one considers the total available variations. Even in the simple linear case above, there are two organic radicals with which to juggle, and for which organic chemistry has many candidates. This represents a minimum; usually, since branching is used, three, four and even more radicals are used. This manifold variety of products accounts for the present widespread use of polyurethanes in industry.

The easiest and commercially most useful method for the production of the urethane linkage is the reaction of the isocyanate radical ($-N=C=O$, may be considered as the anhydride of the unstable carbamic acid) with an alcohol radical (OH). This will be elaborated on in Chapter 2. From the above, we may derive the following working definition that the polyurethanes are polymers produced by the addition reaction between polyisocyanates (difunctional or higher) and hydroxyl-rich compounds (at least two hydroxyl groups per molecule), such as glycols, polyesters, polyethers, etc.

These polymers first came to the attention of the plastics and chemical groups in the United States after World War II. A review article appeared in the October 1945 issue of *Modern Plastics,* describing the progress made in the field of plastics in Germany during the war (1939-1945). The author, G. M. Kline, Chief of the Plastics Section of the National Bureau of Standards, outlined a survey based upon data obtained during a three months' tour made under the auspices of the Office of the Chief of Ordnance, War Department. In this article, as well as in a short note in *Chemical and Engineering News* for September 25, 1945, he discussed, among other plastics, a new group, namely, "polyurethanes." A short summary of preparations, applications and economics was given. This was an extremely useful new polymeric material, developed by the Germans, but apparently completely unknown to us. In fact, the development of polyurethanes was sufficiently exploited so that a well-integrated industry was developed in that country soon after the war. At present, something like 24 million pounds of diisocyanates are used in making polyurethanes.

However, a review of the American patent literature revealed that DuPont, in a series of patents applied for in 1939 and 1940, and granted in the early 1940's, had done much work along these lines. Their patents covered the reaction products of polyisocyanates with the various glycols, alkyd resins, polyamides, polyesters, diamines, polyester-amides, etc. These products were claimed to be suitable for fibers, films, plastics, etc. In these two lines of experimental investigation are to be found the origin of the commercial exploitation of the isocyanate derivatives—the polyurethanes. In addition, American patent literature revealed that in the early 1940's much study was directed toward the use of diisocyanates as adhesive assistants, particularly in adhering elastomers to metals and fibers. The first commercial application of diisocyanates in this country was reported to have developed during the early part of World War II. Methylene bis-(4-phenyl isocyanate) was employed to aid in the adhesion of rubber and neoprene to synthetic fibers. The final products were life rafts and "Mae West" inflatable vests. Despite these American investigations, the real impetus for the commercial development of polyurethanes came from the fruitful studies and products of the Germans, particularly those of Dr. Otto Bayer.

As pointed out previously, the chemistry of polyurethanes is an offshoot of the organic chemistry of isocyanates. Before 1850, the pioneers of organic chemistry, Wurtz and Hoffman, had prepared and elucidated the properties of the reactions of monobasic isocyanates, both aliphatic and aromatic. Intensive study of the isocyanates was discouraged initially because of the difficulties and poor yields inherent in the original preparatory methods. However, in 1884, Hentschel developed the most convenient preparation of isocyanates—that of phosgenation of primary amines; he obtained excellent yields, and interest in this field increased. Without this preparatory method, it is doubtful if much work could have been done on the diisocyanates.

Until the 1930's, no real commercial applications of the

phases in which we are interested were studied. The year 1937 is a good point to place the beginning of the present line of investigation of the polyurethanes; for it was then that Dr. Otto Bayer decided to experiment with addition products of diisocyanates as a means of producing fibers equal to or superior to nylon, which would not be covered by the DuPont patents on nylon. On March 26, 1937, his group discovered the diisocyanate polyaddition process and subsequently obtained the German patent 728,981, covering this work. The group of patents produced at this time, and the aforementioned DuPont patents, marked the beginning of a patent literature which now numbers over 400 patents.

The polyureas proved to yield only infusible and strongly hydrophilic polymers which were not suitable for fibers or plastics. Then, the Germans discovered and developed the linear polyurethanes, which were very versatile plastics of much promise. These were advanced to such an extent that, by 1941, they were being marketed in Germany in two forms. One, called Perlon U, was used for synthetic fibers and bristles; the second, called Igamid U, was used for plastics. In the same year, Dr. Otto Bayer applied for war time priorities for the construction of a plant with a capacity of 200 tons of aliphatic diisocyanates and 100 tons of aromatic diisocyanates (this reflected the emphasis at that time on Perlon U and Igamid U). As a justification for these priorities, he showed how his group had made many other advances in the commercial applications of diisocyanates and their products. Potentials were shown to exist in the fields of adhesives, foams (the Air Force displayed much interest in this phase), lacquers, and coatings, as well as synthetic leather, etc.

In 1945, the Office of the Quartermaster General sent a group of observers to Germany to investigate any technical developments in the field of plastics which might have immediate applications to the plastics research program of the Quartermaster Corps in connection with the war in the Pacific Theater. They found that much of the potential predicted in the isocyanate field was being fulfilled. In addition to the linear polymers made from aliphatic glycols and aliphatic diisocyanates, several applications based on tolylene diisocyanate and a series of polyesters became important, such as foams, coatings and adhesives. Applications in the airplane industry were most interesting; foams were used as fillers in various sandwich laminates in order to combine low weight with high strength. These fillers also demonstrated that the foam cores could withstand vibration. The glasslike finishes on planes resulted in noticeable increases in speeds; also, the resistance of these coatings to fuel, water and general weather conditions was excellent. These are only a sample of the uses that had already been developed. In most of the German work, combinations of several polyesters (Desmophens) and diisocyanates (and derivatives) constantly appear; it would seem desirable therefore to list these polyesters here for future reference.

TABLE 1.1. COMPOSITION OF DESMOPHENS

Number	Adipic Acid	Phthalic Anhydride	Triol*	Butylene** Glycol
200	1.5	1.5	4.0	—
300***	—	3.0	4.1	—
800	2.5	0.5	4.1	—
800 S	2.5	0.5	4.0	—
900	3.0	—	4.0	—
1100	3.0	—	2.0	3.0
1200	3.0	—	1.0	3.0

(Column header group: Moles of)

* Triols used are glycerine, trimethyol propane and hexantriol-l, 2, 6; the latter is usually used with higher number resins.
** 1, 3-butylene glycol is used for #1200; 1, 4-butylene glycol is used for #1100.
*** #300 formula is also given as one part of #900 to one part of xylene-formaldehyde resin.

It will be noted in Table 1.1 that less cross-branching occurs with the higher product numbers, and, hence, produces softer coatings, more elastic foams, etc. The diisocyanates and several of their derivatives, called "Desmodurs," are listed in Table 1.2. These are used as the diisocyanate component in the Desmophen-Desmodur combinations.

TABLE 1.2. COMPOSITION OF THE MORE COMMON DESMODURS

Desmodur	Composition
H	Hexamethylene diisocyanate
HH	1 mole of trimethylol propane 3 moles of hexamethylene diisocyanate
T	Tolylene diisocyanate—(65% 2,4 and 35% 2,6)
TH	1 mole trimethylol propane 3 moles Desmodur T
R	Tri-(p-isocyanylphenyl) methane
15	Naphthalene diisocyanate-1,5

These are the most common, and may recur throughout this discussion. The tendency in coatings is to use Desmodur HH and TH instead of the parent diisocyanates.

Our observers were impressed with the development and applications which had been made in the polyurethane field. The Air Force was interested in foams, and granted a development contract to Goodyear Aircraft for a system of rigid alkyl isocyanate foams. Work was commenced in September 1946, and resulted in a "one-shot" method which will be discussed in Chapter 3. In the latter part of 1947, and the early part of 1948, Lockheed Aircraft Corporation began independently to develop polyurethane foam systems for use in radome construction and in filling aircraft components. This work was successful and produced two-component systems of such a nature that one component was a resin (polyester), and the other a diisocyanate. These components could be blended at room temperature and poured in place for foaming to fill voids. These systems will be discussed in detail in Chapter 3. Stimulated by these activities, as well as by their own research on foams, adhesives and other isocyanate products, DuPont and Monsanto started to produce the diisocyanate raw materials in semi-commercial quantities by 1950. As early as November 1946, DuPont called attention to Kline's article in *Modern Plastics* in their advertisements for diisocyanates, and shortly thereafter issued literature on their studies. However, in the field of cellular products, it was not until October 1953, that DuPont announced a commercial type of foamed polyurethane, though some of their licensees were supplied with information on the preparatory methods prior to this date. This was of the prepolymer type and will be reviewed in Chapter 4. With the successful development of some of the above projects, foamed-in-place polyester-diisocyanate systems became commercially available to fabricators of plastics.

Meanwhile, a well-integrated industry based on diisocyanates was established in Germany. Because of the enormous production of flexible polyurethane foams, the previous emphasis on aliphatic diisocyanates shifted to the aromatics. The equipment and art for continuous production were developed to such a degree that these light-weight elastomers dominated many fields of domestic and transportation uses. The commercial success of the various polyurethanes in Germany aroused a tremendous interest in this country. Several foam machines were imported; and, finally, in 1954, a joint company (Mobay) was formed by Bayer and Monsanto. Through these means, the German know-how (and equipment) was funneled to the United States. This was made available through license agreements. In addition to this, there are two other license structures in the isocyanate field. One is that of DuPont, which covers patents on the basic reaction products of diisocyanates; the other is that of the Lockheed group of patents. In more recent years, National Aniline has entered the field of polyurethanes as a producer of diisocyanates. This company has been doing much research in the chemistry and application of these products. At present, there are three primary producers of diisocyanates (mainly tolylene diisocyanates), namely, Du-Pont, Mobay, and National Aniline. It has been estimated that there is available, at present, a yearly productive capacity of 70 million pounds. In addition, Carwin Chemical Company has been producing special diisocyanates, mainly based upon benzidine and its homologs. Most of the production of polyurethanes in the United States is in foams, but interest in coatings, rubber (castings, as well as tires), and adhesives is growing.

2. CHEMISTRY

The most important, and yet the least known, class of chemicals used in the commercial preparation of polyurethanes is the polyisocyanates, especially the diisocyanates. Many different methods have been used to synthesize isocyanates; all except one are of no great interest, and these may be found in the various textbooks on organic chemistry. A good source is a review on isocyanates by Saunders and Slocombe (*Chem. Rev.*, 43, page 203, 1948). Practically all the present industrial methods utilize the basic method discovered by Hentschel in 1884.

Fundamentally, the preparation involves the reaction of phosgene with an amine or one of its salts. There is an abundance of good procedures to be found in the patent literature. Just as in most chemical processes, where the present trend is toward continuous systems, the same holds for the manufacture of diisocyanates. Present commercial processes for the more important diisocyanates are continuous. Since tolylene diisocyanate is the most important commercial diisocyanate, it may be of interest to follow one of the ways in which it is prepared (that taken from the latest patent literature being considered as typical). Into a heated reaction vessel, equipped with an agitator, thermometer, gas inlet, a liquid inlet tube and a take-off condenser, is charged a chlorinated polyphenyl (such as that sold by Monsanto Chemical Company as "Aroclor" No. 1260), having a boiling range of 385 to 420°C. The temperature

11

is adjusted to 260°C. A solution of 2,4-tolylene diamine in o-dichlorobenzene is fed into this through the liquid inlet tube which dips below the surface of the chlorinated polyphenyl.

The reaction mass is agitated, and the temperature is held at 255 to 265°C during this time of addition. Simultaneously, phosgene is added to the reaction mass at a uniform rate through the gas inlet tube, which also dips below the surface of the liquid. Since the boiling point of tolylene diisocyanate is 250°C (less than the reaction temperature), it distills out of the reaction mass as it forms, together with the o-dichlorobenzene. The vapors are condensed and collected in a receiver where the temperature is maintained at 180 to 185°C to prevent reformation of the corresponding carbamyl chloride. The hydrogen chloride gas formed in the reaction passes over with the diisocyanate and solvent and is removed through a reflux condenser attached to the receiver. The diisocyanate is recovered from solution by vacuum distillation. Yields in the neighborhood of 90 per cent are claimed. The method has the advantage of preventing wasteful side reactions between unreacted diamine and newly formed diisocyanate, which would form urea and tarry by-products, as well as that of being continuous. The reaction is as follows:

| *meta*-Tolylene diamine | *Phosgene* | *meta*-Tolylene diisocyanate | *Hydrogen chloride* |

Already, many mono- and diisocyanates, as well as a few triisocyanates, are commercially available. Several of these diisocyanates are produced by more than one company; and, in addition, the commercial literature frequently ignores the chemical names and uses the various trade names. In order to enable the reader to find his way through this maze of conflicting names, Table 2.1 lists the more important names and chemical synonyms.

TABLE 2.1. DIISOCYANATES AND THEIR TRADE NAMES

Polyisocyanates	Trade Name			
	Desmodur *	Hylene **	Mondur ***	Nacconate ****
Tolylene diissocyanate (65% 2,4; 35% 2,6)	T	TM65	TD	65
Tolylene diisocyanate (80% 2,4; 20% 2,6)		TM	TD 80	80
Tolylene diisocyanate (100% 2,4)		T	TDS	100
3,3'-Bitolylene-4,4'-diisocyanate[a]				200
Diphenylmethane-4,4'-diisocyanate		M	M	300
3,3'-Dimethyldiphenylmethane-4,4'-diisocyanate		DMM		310
Meta-phenylene diisocyanate				400
2,4-Tolylene diisocyanate dimer	TT	TD		
Triphenylmethane triisocyanate	R		TM	
Hexamethylene diisocyanate	H			
Dianisidine diisocyanate[b]				
PAPI-1—Carwin's polyaryl polyisocyanate (tri)				

* Bayer
** duPont
*** Mobay
**** National Aniline
[a] Carwin Trade Name TODI
[b] Carwin Trade Name DADI

Some twelve polyisocyanates are listed. In general, the derivatives, such as DuPont TU which is an addition product of 2,4-tolylene diisocyanate (2 moles) with water (1 mole), are not given. It is felt that the latter derivatives are somewhat specialized and can be best treated in applications or in safety discussions where their need will be shown. Most of the above chemicals are being used in small quantities; less than a handful are used in any appreciable quantities. The largest production is represented by the various isomer combinations of tolylene diisocyanates 2,4 and 2,6. Since

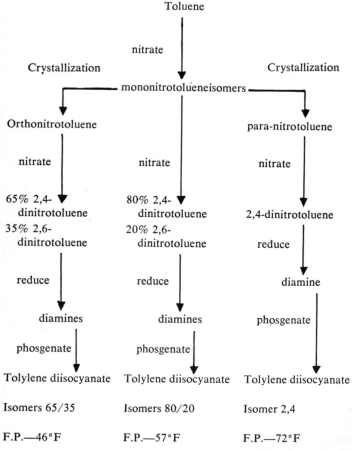

Figure 2.1. Preparation of Tolylene Diisocyanate Isomers

these products are primarily found in the form of three different isomer ratios, it would help one to understand the economics involved if he knew how they were produced.

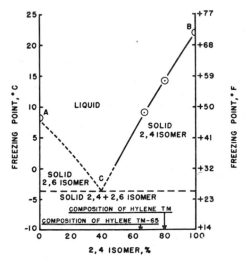

Figure 2.2. Freezing point-composition diagram for 2,4- and 2,6-toluene diisocyanates.

It is obvious that a continuous process can be set up most economically to make the 80/20 isomer ratio. In order to market any other isomer ratio of the tolylene diisocyanates, a manufacturer must be able to utilize the by-products. The present thinking is that the 80/20 isomer ratio may be termed the "workhorse of the polyurethane field." It is expected that this will be the diisocyanate product most widely used in commercial applications. When using a mixture of isomers, such as 80/20 or 65/35, under conditions where the temperature is below their freezing points, it is necessary to melt it completely and to stir it well before using. Figure 2.2 illustrates this point.

The eutectic point is 40 per cent 2,4-isomer and 60 per cent 2,6-isomer; hence, a partial melt composition would be far from that expected with a rated composition. This would have a tremendous effect upon the final polyurethane product. For example, in flexible foams, different operating conditions are necessary for the various isomer ratios. Other diisocyanates will be mentioned in the discussion on the applications of polyurethanes, but these must have sufficient advantages over the 80/20 isomers of tolylene diisocyanate to warrant their use, despite their higher prices. Some examples are hexamethylene diisocyanates in fibers, diphenyl methane 4,4'-diisocyanate in adhesives, and naphthalene 1,5-diisocyanates in urethane rubbers.

The diisocyanates are employed in chemical reactions because they will react with and add to any chemical compound containing an active hydrogen. The easiest way to define a chemical compound containing an active hydrogen is to use the operational method. The compound, under question, would be one that gives a positive Zerewitinoff test. In other words, any chemical which, when added to a Grignard solution of methyl iodide, will liberate methane by decomposition of the Grignard reagent. Some examples are those having hydroxyl groups (water, alcohols and phenols), amino groups (primary and secondary), carboxylic acid groups, hydrogens on certain activated methylene groups, such as acetoacetic ester, malonic ester, etc. The addition reaction of the isocyanate group with a monofunctional reagent is as follows:

$$R-N=C=O + HX \longrightarrow R-\overset{H}{N}-\overset{X}{C}=O$$

Of course, where the polyfunctionality comes into play is for the creation of polymer chains of large molecular size and sometimes of infinite molecules.

The amines, both primary and secondary, are the most reactive of the above hydrogen compounds toward the addition reaction with the isocyanate group.

$$R-N=C=O \ + \ HNR_1R_2 \longrightarrow R-\underset{H}{N}-\overset{O}{\overset{\|}{C}}-N\underset{R_2}{\overset{R_1}{<}} \quad , R_1 \text{ and } R_2 \text{ may be } H$$

In these cases, substituted ureas (mainly non-symmetrical) result. It is possible to take the reactions one step further, since the hydrogen in the urea is sufficiently basic to react with more isocyanate to form a biuret.

$$R-N-\overset{O}{\overset{\|}{C}}-\underset{}{\overset{H}{N}}-R$$

Tertiary amines, having no active hydrogens, cannot add to the isocyanate group, but they do act as catalysts for the general reaction. In the early phases of his program, Dr. Otto Bayer found that the polyureas were not suitable for plastics. Thus, the reaction of diisocyanates with diamines and mono-amines is used commercially to only a small extent. The analytical chemist, however, uses this reaction to assay isocyanates and its derivatives. In this case, the isocyanate group is determined quantitatively by backtitrating the un-reacted dibutylamine after an excess is reacted with the sample in question, under mild conditions. (See Appendix for S.P.I. method for amine equivalent.)

The most important reaction employing diisocyanates is that with hydroxyl-containing compounds which forms the corresponding urethanes. We are interested in such products as the glycols, polyols, hydroxyl-rich polyesters, as well as the various polyethers, used to produce the polymers now commonly called "polyurethanes." The chemical equation employing monofunctional components is as follows:

$$R_1-OH + R-N=C=O \longrightarrow \overset{H}{R}\overset{}{N}-\overset{O}{\overset{\|}{C}}-OR_1$$

This is a simple addition process which, when extended to functional or polyfunctional chemicals, provides a direct route to polymers. The molecular weights and configurations are controlled, similar to ordinary condensation polymerization, without the liberation of interfering by-products usually associated with these condensations, or severe conditions necessary to force the polymerizations to high molecular weights. (See application to fibers). As in the case of the polyureas, the hydrogens on the nitrogen atoms of the urethane groups are capable of reacting with more isocyanates to form allophanates.

$$\begin{array}{c} O \\ \| \\ RN-C-OR_1 \\ | \\ C=O \\ | \\ RNH \end{array}$$

This shows another possible means of introducing branching in polyurethanes. The urethane reaction has been studied with reference to the reactivity of the various alcohols. It has been found that primary alcohols react about three times as fast as secondary ones, while the tertiary alcohols react very slowly and tend to dehydrate.

The urethane reaction is definitely base-catalyzed and, in the case of aliphatic alcohols, appears to be inhibited to some extent by acids. Tertiary amines are among the better catalysts; here, the base strength of the particular tertiary amine is not necessarily the sole criterion for catalytic activity. Steric effects are also important. Thus, it has been shown that pyridine is superior to the dialkyl anilines, which are of equal strength. Recent investigations using tolylene diisocyanate and a hydroxyl-rich polyester (diethylene glycol adipate) reveal this in a qualitative manner.

TABLE 2.2. BASIC STRENGTH AND CATALYTIC ACTIVITY
OF VARIOUS ISOCYANATE CATALYSTS

	Order of Increasing Basic Strength	Order of Increasing Catalytic Activity
N-Methyl morpholine	1	1
Dimethyl ethanolamine	2	2
Triethylamine	3	4
N, N'-Diethylcyclohexylamine	3	3

Table 2.2 was derived from Figure 2.3. It can be noted from this figure that cobalt naphthenate has considerable catalytic activity.

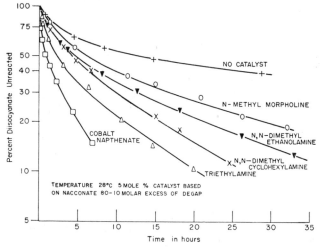

Figure 2.3. Reaction rate of "Nacconate 80"-diethylene glycol adipate polyester with various catalysts.

When the effects of acidity upon the urethane reaction with aliphatic hydroxyl compounds are examined, we find that traces of mineral acids act as weak inhibitors. The use of percentages of less than 0.1 per cent has been found to affect the reactivity of tolylene diisocyanate toward glycols. At present, the usual grades of TDI have very small percentages (mere traces) of mineral acidity. A few years ago, this was not true. Apparently, some hydrochloric acid gas came through during distillation to form some carbamyl chloride.

$$-N-C\diagup O \diagdown Cl$$
$$H$$

Two methods have been suggested for determining this impurity. The first is for hydrolyzable chloride which, apparently, includes some impurity other than the carbamyl chloride. The second is one acidity measurement which should be a direct measure. The former is the official S.P.I. procedure; the second is not. These methods may be found in pertinent literature.

We emphasized above that aliphatic alcohols were involved. However, phenols can be reacted to form urethanes. The yields may be poor even with the employment of heat. Catalysts must be used to improve the yields. What is surprising is that acids (the stronger the better), as well as bases, can be effective. In fact, the order of catalytic activity exhibited by acids and bases is equivalent. The preparation of phenyl urethanes is important because they belong to the class of hindered isocyanates used in coating applications, which will be discussed in Chapter 8.

The other chemical in the polyurethane reaction is a diisocyanate. Though it is expected that the tolylene diisocyanate isomer group will be the most important, there is no reason why others cannot be used. Hence, an under-

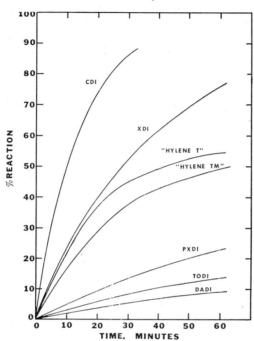

Figure 2.4. Relative reactivity of Carwin diisocyanates.
(See Table for symbol legend.)

VELOCITY CONSTANTS FOR THE REACTION OF BIPHENYLENE DIISOCYANATES WITH SEC.-BUTANOL AT 25°C

Symbol	Diisocyanate Name	k 1./equiv./sec.
DADI	Dianisidine Diisocyanate (3,3'-Dimethoxy-4,4'-biphenylenediisocyanate)	6.3×10^{-6}
TODI	Bitolylene Diisocyanate (3,3'-Dimethyl-4,4'-biphenylenediisocyanate)	1.3×10^{-5}
PXDI	Diphenylxenylene Diisocyanate (3,3'-Diphenyl-4,4'-biphenylenediisocyanate)	2.1×10^{-5}
XDI	Xenylene Diisocyanate (4,4'-Biphenylenediisocyanate)	1.1×10^{-4}
CDI	Dichloroxenylene Diisocyanate (3,3'-Dichloro-4,4'-biphenylenediisocyanate)	2.4×10^{-4}

standing of the relative reactivities of these chemicals against tolylene diisocyanate is in order. Figure 2.4 gives the results of several studies made using secondary butanol at 25°C. Figure 2.5 illustrates a similar study, using a primary alcohol (2-ethylhexanol) as the substrate.

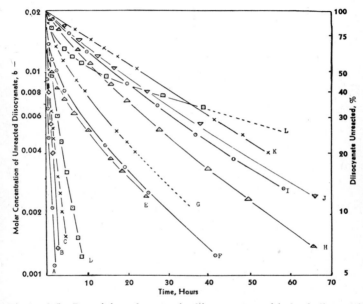

Figure 2.5. Reactivity of aromatic diisocyanates with 2-ethylhexanol and diethylene glycol adipate polyester. (*Courtesy Bailey, I.E.C., Apr. 1956.*)

A. 1-Chloro-2,4-phenylene diisocyanate
B. *m*-Phenylene diisocyanate
C. *p*-Phenylene diisocyanate
D. 4,4′ Methylenebis (phenyl isocyanate)
E. 2,4-Tolylene diisocyanate
F. Tolylene diisocyanate (60% 2,4-isomer, 40% 2,6-isomer)
G. 2,6-Tolylene diisocyanate
H. 3,3′-Dimethyl-4,4′-biphenylene diisocyanate
I. 4,4′-Methylenebis (2-methylphenyl isocyanate)
J. 3,3′-Dimethoxy-4,4′-biphenylene diisocyanate
K. 2,2′, 5,5′-Tetramethyl-4,4′-biphenylene diisocyanate
L. 80% 2,4- and 20% 2,6-isomer of tolylene diisocyanate with diethylene glycol adipate polyester

This is another means of varying the reactivity of the urethane reaction, as well as the composition of the product. It may be noted that the 2,6-tolylene diisocyanates are weaker than 2,4; removal of the methyl group enhances the activity, and replacement by chlorine increases it further. In trying to interpret the activity of a particular isocyanate compound, care must be taken not to overlook the steric hindrance factor—the main reason for lower reactivity of the 2,6-isomer of tolylene diisocyanate.

Polyureas, polyurethanes and their products with more diisocyanates are formed by the simple addition reaction without any by-products. On the other hand, the next two important reaction polymers produced are accompanied by a gaseous by-product (carbon dioxide) which may be an advantage or a disadvantage, depending on the contemplated use. The first reaction involves the interaction of carboxylic acids with isocyanate. This reaction will be shown by means of monofunctional reagents.

These reactions may be more complex than the above two equations indicate; but, for the most part, these end products represent the actual products. The two reagents combine to

form a type of acid anhydride which decomposes when
heated to produce carbon dioxide gas and an acid amide.
The need for extra heat to complete the reaction may be
shown in the experimental fact that, if the reaction is run
in the cold, the later addition of either alcohol or amine
will decompose the acid anhydride and produce corresponding urethane or urea without the liberation of gas. In many
cases, the presence of carboxylic acid value is preferably
suppressed and, at most, tolerated. However, there is one
case where it is deliberately added in the form of acetic
acid to form the gas necessary to produce cellular rigid
polyurethanes. The acid amide formed above may be further
reacted with isocyanate to form acyl amide.

The really important gas-forming reaction is that between
water and isocyanate, in which water adds to the isocyanate
group to form a carbamic acid. The latter, being unstable,
decomposes to the corresponding amine and carbon dioxide.
The amine reacts with another isocyanate group to form a
symmetrical urea. Thus, we find that water reacts with two
equivalents of isocyanate. With polyisocyanates, the reactions
form polymeric materials which are infusible and insoluble.
Using a monofunctional isocyanate, the following chemical
reaction occurs:

$$R-N=C=O + HOH \longrightarrow R-\overset{H}{N}-\overset{O}{\overset{\|}{C}}-OH$$

$$R-\overset{H}{N}-\overset{O}{\overset{\|}{C}}-H \longrightarrow RNH_2 + CO_2\uparrow$$

$$RNH_2 + R-N=C=O \longrightarrow R-\overset{H}{N}-\overset{O}{\overset{\|}{C}}-\overset{H}{N}-R$$

The hydrogen atoms on the ureido nitrogens may react
further with more isocyanate to form biurets. This is the
reason that water may act as a branching chemical in isocyanate polymers. Advantage is taken of this in polyurethane

rubbers and foams to introduce cross-linking. In general, this reaction with water is important and must be taken into account in all isocyanate work, either to avoid gas bubbles or to produce gas for foaming. Besides this, the fact that only a very small quantity of water is necessary to affect the shelf life of true isocyanate prepolymers (resins) is sometimes overlooked. These are products where some isocyanate groups are pre-reacted, as in some of the Desmodurs. Most prepolymers have an equivalent weight of about 300 or more; hence, 9 grams of water will react with 300 grams of resin. This means that only 3 per cent by weight of water is required to completely react with the prepolymer. Even humidity in the air, if not guarded against, will quickly cause skinning. Water is an important factor in any isocyanate study.

From the above, it can be seen that the reactions of polyester and diisocyanates are manifold, especially when the possibility of water is taken into account. We have a series of competing reactions where the initial reagents and products may further react. Studies have been made to elucidate the activity scale for the various groups. A most interesting one is that of Morton and Deisz, of the Institute of Rubber Research at the University of Akron. They determined the comparative reaction rate in dioxane at 80°C with phenyl isocyanate.

Table 2.3 does not give the complete picture, as gradations within classes are possible with over-lapping. Thus, primary alcohols are about three times as reactive as secondary, while tertiary are fairly inactive. Another factor is solubility; this may be especially important in toxicity problems where water may be expected to react with and deactivate split diisocyanates. However, because of the low mutual solubilities, the water may spread them and only react very slowly. A third factor of importance is the effect of catalysts upon the relative rates. Dr. Bayer reports that water is three times as reactive as hydroxyl groups when certain catalysts are present in foam work. Another factor which adds to the complexity of the work is that the reaction products are catalysts for the reaction. All in all, the kinetic problem of the apparent straightforward reaction of diisocyanate and polyester is quite complex.

TABLE 2.3. COMPARATIVE REACTION RATES WITH PHENYL ISOCYANATE

Reactant	Class	Relative Rate
n-Butyl phenyl carbamate	Urethane	1
Acetanilide	Amide	16
n-Butyric acid	Carboxylic acid	26
Carbanilide	Urea	80
Water	Water	98
n-Butanol	Alcohol	460

The addition reactions of isocyanate with the various compounds having active hydrogens is reversible when heat is applied. Thus, even such compounds as urethanes of primary alcohols will regenerate isocyanate when they are heated above 250°C. Advantage is taken of this in many commercial applications. The Germans had discovered this experimental fact as early as 1938, and started to produce adducts with lower temperature stability. These products are called "hindered isocyanates," or "isocyanate generators." Thus, adducts formed from phenol and isocyanates are stable at room temperature, but will regenerate isocyanates at 160°C; the latter may then react with a hydroxyl group to form a more stable linkage. The Mobay product, Mondur S, is an example of this type. Thus it is possible to have a one-component system consisting of a polyester and an isocyanate generator of indefinite shelf-life. For example, when a coating of this type is heated to 160°C, cross-linking reactions occur, phenol is lost, and a cured coating results. Other adducts of lower temperature stability are known; thus, those of malonic ester only require temperatures in the range of 130°C.

In the group with malonic esters may be found ethyl acetoacetate. The preparation of isocyanate generators from these precursors is not direct. It is necessary to react a suspension of the sodio derivative of these esters in ether, with the diisocyanate in equivalent ratios. The final product is liberated by acidulation with acetic acid. A related type of isocyanate generator is the dimers of isocyanate. The best example would be that from 2,4-tolylene diisocyanate. Under the influence of either pyridine or triethyl phosphine, the isocyanates in the four position of two molecules dimerize, leaving the two position isocyanates free to react. Then, at about 150°C, the dimer dissociates and liberates two equivalents of isocyanates for cross-linking, etc. When the commercial applications of the polyurethanes are studied, we will be able to appreciate these systems more. Mention will be made here of one application. An Australian patent proposes the addition of the above isocyanate generator precursors to isocyanate resins (those with free isocyanate groups) to improve their shelf-life.

The error of believing that polyurethanes can only be made by the reaction of polyisocyanates with hydroxyl rich compounds should not be made. For example, there is what may be termed the "inverse reaction" to the normal one. Let us view the simple monofunctional urethane formation from the most basic chemicals, ignoring the intermediate preparation of the isocyanate compound. We see that an alcohol and an amine (except tertiary) are coupled together by phosgene (the acid chloride of carbonic acid) to form a urethane, with the elimination of hydrogen chloride. Now, if, instead of first reacting an amine with phosgene (the isocyanate path), we react an alcohol first with phosgene, then with an amine, we obtain an alternate preparatory method for urethane. Thus, phosgene will react with alcohols to form the corresponding esters of chlorocarbonic acid, which are then reacted with amines to produce the equivalent urethanes of the isocyanate method.

$$\underset{Cl}{\overset{Cl}{C}}{=}O \;+\; ROH \longrightarrow \underset{OR}{\overset{Cl}{C}}{=}O \;+\; HCl$$

$$\underset{OR}{\overset{Cl}{C}}{=}O \;+\; NHR_1R_2 \longrightarrow \underset{OR}{\overset{N\diagdown R_1}{C}}{=}O\,R_2 \;+\; HCl$$

To obtain polymers, as before, glycols are used (to form bis esters) and triols (for branching) for the hydroxyl compounds, together with diamines for the final condensation. In Chapter 9 it will be seen how products similar to Perlon U may be obtained by these means. This method lacks the versatility and ease of handling of the isocyanates addition processes but avoids the use of diisocyanates which are difficult or impossible to produce.

3. RIGID FOAMS

Though the initial reports of the German wartime work on polyurethanes contained little information regarding rigid foams, it was in this field that the first postwar efforts were made in America. It may have been the promise of foamed-in-place light-weight plastics that required comparatively simple equipment and preparatory conditions that prompted this development. The initial, meager reports indicated that the Germans used, basically, their now familiar system of Desmophen (polyester) and Desmodur (diisocyanate) to produce a cellular plastic (Moltopren), aided by the gas-producing reactions of the isocyanate group with carboxylic acids and water. The polyesters had acid values of at least 30, and usually contained some water of esterification which remained after completion of the reaction, being held in solution by the hydroxyl-rich product. The foams were produced by stirring the diisocyanate (usually meta-tolylene diisocyanates) into the viscous polyester until the exothermic reaction which formed the urethane linkages took place. This started the gas-forming reactions. Thus, the reaction mass became tougher and tougher, swelling up like dough and also hardening. Although the material could be molded when first foamed, it quickly became hard and infusible. The foam was usually sold to aircraft manufacturers in block form, approximately 700 x 700 x 100 mm in size, for use as a core material, with facings of metal and plywood, in the construction of wings and stabilizers for airplanes. It was also used in submarine construction for sound insulation and in tanks for heat insulation. Some foamed-in-place applications were also reported. Indications were given that foams with varying amounts of rigidity could be produced; usually, the higher the Desmophen number, the softer the foam. In some cases, extra water was added to produce lower density foams. The most important information derived from this preliminary work was the range of physical properties obtainable with these cellular products, and the promise inherent with these.

TABLE 3.1. COMPRESSIVE STRENGTH OF MOLTOPREN

Moltopren Number	Density (pcf)	Compressive Strength (psi)	$\frac{C.S.}{D}$
50	3.0	36	12
60	3.6	57	16
80	4.8	86	18
100	6.0	114	19
120	7.2	170	24
150	9.0	260	29
200	12.0	400	33
250	15.0	570	38
300	18.0	860	48

The Moltopren number was the foam density expressed in kilograms per cubic meter. The data (Table 3.1) indicated the interesting characteristic that the higher densities produce strength properties greater than those which may be expected from a mere increase in density. Thus, the first and last items differ by a factor of 6 in density, but by a factor of 20 in strength (see fourth column of Table 3.1). In addition to the good strength characteristics exhibited at room temperature, it was claimed that some of these foams were good up to 140°C (280°F). Also, their heat insulation qualities were reported to be twice as good as cork. Thus, the German work indicated much promise, but did not give more than vague preparatory methods for the rigid polyurethane foams. There was an indication of the availability of a self-blowing system which could produce a thermosetting low density foamed-in-place cellular plastic of good physical characteristics.

By September, 1946, Goodyear Aircraft Corporation embarked upon an Air Force sponsored development project, one phase of which was directed toward the development of new low-density core materials that could be used in radome construction. One result of this project was the development of a polyester resin which could be foamed with tolylene diisocyanate. In addition, a definite method of foaming was developed. The polyester had the following composition:

> 3.8 moles glycerine
> 2.5 moles adipic acid
> 0.5 mole phthalic anhydride

with an acid value of about 40, and a water content of 1.3 to 1.8 per cent. The following laboratory procedure was recommended for foaming. The components were as follows:

> 140 grams tolylene diisocyanate
> 150 grams resin
> 16 cc Aerosol Solution (10% Aerosol OT*
>   in acetone)

A 600-cc beaker, equipped with a polyethylene tent held in place by a rubber band, was used. The tent had to be high enough to allow normal manipulation of a spatula, held

---

* Aerosol OT is dioctyl sulfosuccinate (American Cyanamid).

from the outside. The beaker was cooled with an ice bath, which was necessary to keep the temperature of the reaction mass below 30°C during mixing. The resin and diisocyanate were weighed into the beaker and mixed by spatula. Four stages were observed during this process.

1. Incompatibility about 10 minutes
2. Compatability about 12 minutes
3. Opaque
4. Smooth creamy appearance

At this point, the "Aerosol OT" solution was stirred in for a period of 1 to 2 minutes. The contents of the beaker was poured into a preheated mold (150 to 160°F), which was stoked lightly with the spatula to remove air bubbles. After the foam rises it is cured one hour at 150°F, and two hours at 240°F. Seventy-five cubic inches of 10-pound density foam should be obtained from the above quantities. The compressive strength of the foam was about 275 psi, which was in line with that for the Moltoprens. This procedure had been employed on a large scale using Hobart mixers. The tent was necessary because humidity (especially above 50%) caused trouble as a result of the long mixing time required; it was also used to help eliminate the fumes of the diisocyanate, ventilation being essential. Modifications of this method have been suggested; the most interesting one was the direct cooling of the reaction mass by the addition of dry ice. Here, special care was necessary to avoid the usual condensed water found on the surface of dry ice. This method was only adaptable to batch runs.

This dry ice method was employed more recently in the preparation of heat-resistant, foamed-in-place polyurethane foams. The above foam had a heat distortion point of 275°F (true if 10 per cent excess diisocyanate is used over theory). It has been reported in a Wright Air Development Center Report that it was possible to obtain a polyurethane foam which retains considerable portion of its strength at 400°F. The alkyd polyester was made as follows:

Component	MOL Per Cent
Glycerol	51.512
Adipic acid	10.304
Maleic anhydride	25.756
Phthalic anhydride	3.222
Triallyl cyanurate	8.636
Diallyl maleate	0.570

The first four ingredients were condensed at 160 to 170°C until an acid value of 65 had been reached. The resin was cooled to 100°C, the other two ingredients were added, and the reaction mass stirred for one-half hour. The procedure mentioned previously was used to foam this new resin. About 85 grams of tolylene diisocyanate was mixed with every 100 grams of resin, dry ice being added to keep the temperature below 95°F. A temperature range of 75 to 85°F was preferred. In about 25 to 30 minutes, the two components became compatible, and 2 to 3 per cent of ditertiary-butyl peroxide (based on resin) was added. The mixture turned white in 35 to 40 minutes. When a viscosity of 1,500 poises at 85°F was reached, 10 per cent (based on resin) of a 10 per cent solution of "Aerosol OT" was added. Mixing was continued until 300 to 500 poises viscosity was reached. Then the batch was poured. The cure cycle was:

1 hour at 150-160°F
2 hours at 300°F
3 hours at 400°F

This foam had a compressive strength of 150 psi at 400°F, as against one of 270 psi at 75°F, which was quite commendable.

About the same time that Goodyear Aircraft Corporation started their investigations, chemists at Lockheed Aircraft Corporation also decided to study the feasibility of poured-in-place rigid polyurethane foams. In a series of patents, they disclosed a somewhat different approach to the problem. To the mixture of polyester alkyd and tolylene diisocyanate was added various materials called "foam stabilizers," "foaming regulators," and "blending agents." Some of these materials are metallic soaps (zinc stearate, calcium stearate, etc.); metallic powders (aluminum leafing and other leafing powders); high-molecular weight thermoplastic film-forming polymeric resins (some of which are ethyl cellulose, chlorinated natural rubber, polyvinyl acetate and chloride, etc.); metallic salt hydrates that are anhydrous and ethyl alcohol-soluble (the hydrates of sodium acetate, cupric nitrate, magnesium bromide, etc.); and quaternary ammonium bentonite complexes (those obtained by the reaction of bentonite with organic bases or salts of organic bases through base exchange, in which calcium, sodium, potassium, magnesium and other replaceable bases of the silicate component or components of the bentonite enter into double decomposition with the cations of organic bases). This partial list indicates the vast number of additives which are covered by these patents. The use of these materials in the diisocyanate-polyester blend was found to improve the blendability of the two ingredients, regulate the reactions yielding more efficient utilization of the gas produced by the water and carboxyl group, produce a finer and more uniform cell distribution, and, in many instances, act as a strength-producing filler.

In contrast to the previous method of mixing the diisocyanate-polyester, where blending for a long time and cooling were found necessary, the Lockheed system requires only room temperatures and quick blending. There are several Lockheed-type formulations available on the market, and a description of their blending procedure, on a small scale, will illustrate this fact. Roughly, equal quantities of a viscous R component and a less viscous T component are added to a beaker at room temperature. The ingredients are stirred together by means of a spatula using a blending action rather than a whipping action. As the blending progresses, the reaction mass thins out, tends to become clear and to warm up. Just past the clear point, the material is poured into the mold. The mixing time is of the order of 1 to 2 minutes, and about the same time is required for the foam to rise. Thus, in a matter of minutes, the entire foam is produced in place and ready for post-cure, if such is necessary. The increase in efficiency of the gas to produce lower density foams is quite important. Thus, a series of experiments was reported, based on a resin of the following composition:

Glycerol—4 moles
Adipic acid—2.5 moles
Phthalic anhydride—0.5 mole

with an acid value of 14 and 0.32 per cent water. In this series, 30 grams of this resin, with 0.507 gram of water, is reacted with 20 grams of tolylene diisocyanate in the presence of various additives.

TABLE 3.2. EFFECT OF ADDITIVES

Additive	Volume of Foam Produced
None	8.5 cu in.
Alkylated phenoxy polyethoxoxy ethanol	12 cu in.
Manganous chloride	10 cu in.

Another series, using the same resin, but with a water content of 0.13 per cent, revealed that the addition of one gram of zinc stearate per 30 grams of resin, and 20 grams of tolylene diisocyanate, yielded a volume of 9.8 cubic inches while, in the absence of this additive, only 3.75 cubic inches were obtained. In addition to the lower density, the cell size was smaller and more evenly distributed. This system of foaming had another advantage over previous ones in that it was not necessarily restricted to the batch-type. It has been found possible to meter the ingredients, passing them through a mixing chamber and into a mold ready to foam.

At this point, the factors that affect the density and structure of the foam will be considered. These will include the effects due to the physical make-up of the mold, temperatures, water contents, cure, etc.; the effects of catalysts will be considered later. Some of the following remarks will be applicable only to the Lockheed-type of foams; but, in general, they will not. When they are, the reader will easily be able to note them. The first factor to be considered will be the mold make-up and handling, which should be common to all types of polyurethane foams. The materials used to build the mold into which the foaming mass is poured may be divided into two groups, depending on whether it is a conductor or non-conductor of heat. The so-called "insulation-type" of mold, such as is made of wood, masonite, etc., will produce lower density foams than metal molds. The polyurethane process is autocatalytic; that is, the heat produced by the reaction speeds up the reaction and if the heat of reaction (called "exotherm") is not lost through the mold walls, a more efficient blow effect is obtained. Thus, the statement can be made that, if the exotherm can be contained, lower density foams may be expected; conversely, if heat is lost because of metal walls, higher densities may be expected.

The next factor is the ratio of surface to volume. The higher the surface ratio, the higher the density of the resulting foam. Hence, if an attempt is made to foam thin slabs, higher densities must be expected.

The last factor in mold design is the amount of restrain. In most foam set-ups, the entire mold is put together in a supporting jig with openings for pouring in the polyurethane reaction mass. These openings also serve as escape holes for the rising foam and displaced air. The Lockheed foam systems use many different resins, which permit a wide latitude of viscosities in the polyurethane foaming mass. Holes one-quarter inch and larger have been used. The smaller the holes and total volume of the holes, the higher the foam density. At the other extreme is the free rise, where the lowest density may be expected. In some cases, a foaming reaction mass is added to a mold, and then a lid is clamped on top with many small escape holes for the displaced air. Depending on the viscosity of the rising foam, holes of such a size may be bored which will effectively stop the foam through frictional force, while at the same time allowing the air to escape. Again, if the overflow is considered as a means of losing heat, the original statement relating to heat losses and foam density holds. It must be remembered that when we speak of a given density foam formulation, what we mean precisely is that, with a mold of a given shape, made of given materials, and with a given restrain (foam escape) pattern, a foam of a certain density may be expected with the particular foam formulation in question.

To a lesser extent, this may be varied slightly by the quantity of diisocyanate polyester reaction mass which is put into the mold if an allowance is made for overflow. Usually, depending on the operator (in batch operation), it is found that 10 to 30 per cent excess over theory necessary to fill the mold is required for a good fill. Little variation is found in foam densities within these limits. When continuous metering and mixing are employed, lower foam densities are observed. Apparently, a more efficient utilization of the water reaction is obtained. These facts indicate that the foam density may be affected by means other than mold design. The temperature of the ingredients has a marked influence on the foam density and structure. Increasing the temperatures (above room temperature) speeds up the foaming and produces lower foam densities. An accompanying bad feature is that the structure of the foam tends to become quite coarse and irregular. This is true to a lesser degree when the mold temperature is varied. Except for the previously mentioned low-temperature runs derived from the Goodyear studies, little or no work is known employing low temperatures (below room temperature). Thus, the above statement on mold design may be modified to include the mold temperature, temperature of ingredients, and means of blending.

In considering the chemical aspects of the foaming systems, several factors in addition to the construction of the alkyd resins (polyesters) must be taken into account. The composition of the latter may be found in various patents; in many cases, this information is restricted. The foam system will often determine the resin construction; thus, if modified diisocyanate systems are employed, the high viscosity resin suggested by the Goodyear research would not necessarily have to be used. On the other hand, too low a viscous resin would not trap the gas if it were used in the Lockheed system, with the result that no true foam would be produced. Not only are the tolylene diisocyanates used, but also their derivatives. Thus, a Lockheed patent discloses the use of high-molecular weight polyisocyanate reaction products made by reacting tolylene diisocyanates with glycols, bifunctional metallic soaps, polyfunctional aliphatic amino alcohols, etc. This means that, in the general studies of quantitative relationships necessary for foam formulations, not only diisocyanates may be used but also their derivatives. Hence, it is found that it is simplest to use the concept of amine equivalent. The amine equivalent of any isocyanate compound (pure or derivative) is the measure of its ability to react as isocyanate; thus, it is the same as its apparent equivalent chemical weight in the ordinary sense. Since the molecular weight of tolylene diisocyanate is 174, its chemical equivalent weight is 87, as is its amine equivalent. Since a simple titration method is available to obtain this (see Appendix), the value can be most conveniently used. To find the amount of isocyanate compound needed for a normal foam formulation, it is necessary to know the quantity of hydroxyl and carboxyl groups, as well as the water content. Let us take the first two groups first, which are given in terms of milligrams of potassium hydroxide per gram of material. To convert this to the required amine equivalent, one simply converts to the number of grams of potassium hydroxide for 100 grams of material, and changes from potassium hydroxide to the amine equivalent in question. This may be summarized by the following equation:

$$\frac{(OH + COOH)}{10} \times \frac{A.E.}{56.1} = \text{grams of isocyanate compound per 100 grams of material}$$

The calculation of the quantity of isocyanate compound needed for the water content must take into account the fact that water reacts with two isocyanate groups; hence, it has an equivalent weight of 9. Its requirement equation is as follows:

$$\% \text{ water content} \times \frac{A.E.}{9} = \text{grams of isocyanate compound 100 grams of material}$$

These equations, when used for a given resin with a given water content, will determine the theoretical quantity of isocyanate compound (whether pure diisocyanate or derivative) necessary for this resin. Many times an excess of isocyanates is used; 5 per cent is a normal excess. This basic type of calculation can be used for all so-called "one-shot" systems if the hydroxyl, carboxyl and water content of each ingredient is taken into consideration. The factor of excess and deficit of isocyanate groups in a given formulation is a very important one, and will recur from time to time in this discussion. It will occur in the discussion of the effect of water content on the foam density, which is the next factor. As a general rule, for the two systems under consideration here, a small excess is favorable for heat distortion characteristics. Increasing the excess tends to improve the heat distortion but renders the foam more brittle. Not all foams will absorb large excesses of diisocyanate; this excess acts as a plasticizer, increasing the density and requiring a long cure at high temperatures to bind it into the foam. When this is not feasible, it may be said that the maximum excess possible is dependent upon the resin structure.

The reaction between water and isocyanate is by far the best gas-producing means for blowing up the polyurethane resin. The only important exception is the reported use of acetic acid which was used in an investigation made in France. Of course, the carboxyl groups of the resins produce gas during the foaming process; but, in general, this is minor in comparison to the quantity produced by water. Thus, an attempt is made to adjust for density by the correct quantity of water. The relationship between water and density is an empirical one, dependent on the resin and other ingredients present. A typical curve is shown in Figure 3.1.

It should be noted that, in the higher density range (low water content), the dependency of the density on water is quite acute. Hence, it is difficult to obtain high-density foams in free-blow or low-restrain patterns. On the other hand, there appears to be limiting low density where the use of additional water is quite inefficient and even useless. At this point, it is frequently found that the use of a deficit of diisocyanate will produce even lower densities. However, this is accompanied by extreme shrinkages and by very poor heat distortion characteristics. In the center of the graph (Figure 3.1) it is easily possible to obtain desired densities by interpolation. As indicated in the Lockheed patents and latter research, modifiers can be used to extend the density ranges mainly in the lower region.

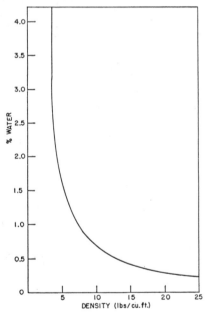

Figure 3.1. Moisture—density curve.

The polyurethane rigid foams should preferably be foamed, partially restrained, and adhered in place. Good adhesion is generally obtained if the surface is clean and slightly roughened. In the case of aluminum, and most other metals, a slight sand-blasting is adequate. This is also true for polyester laminates. In some cases, it has been found advantageous to use adhesives. When this is necessary, the

Figures 3.2a-f show the formation of a radome.

Figure 3.2a. Preparing the skins.

operator should be sure that the adhesive film is free of solvent and water. The above foams can also be made with the aid of mold release agents, producing foams with a dense polyurethane skin. Polyethylene and "Teflon" are excellent surfaces for this purpose, producing foam skins which are very smooth and hard. Silicone resin is also a good mold release, but the use of silicone oils is generally found to be

Figure 3.2b. Pouring foam into mold through strainer. Note inner and outer skins in place on mold.

bad. The foam, in rising, exerts a scouring action on the side of the molds, removing the oil and adhering to the freshly exposed surface. In addition to metal surfaces, wood and plaster of Paris molds may be used for casting. When these are used it is necessary to seal the pores of the substrate with a good phenolic varnish and then to use silicone resin. When castings of rigid polyurethanes are made, a draft must be provided because of the very low shrinkage. Foams in the range of 10 pounds show no visible shrinkage;

Figure 3.2c. Curing the part. Excess foam is coming out of the mold at top.

in fact, with insulation-type molds, static electricity occurs when the mold is broken as a result of the close fit. The skins of these castings reproduce fine marks on the surfaces of the mold even including those exhibited by brush marks

incurred during application of the resin. In both cases, adhered or cast, adequate provision should be made for venting
of air to prevent occlusion of air pockets. Despite this
discussion on mold releases, it is still felt that the best
method of foaming rigid foams is to adhere them in place.

Figure 3.2d. Removing the cured part from the mold.

There are two general methods of applying rigid polyurethanes. The first is known as the male-female type. A
good illustration of this can be found in the construction of
a radome (Figure 3.2). The important principle is that one

part of the mold (female) is completely open, and the male part of the mold is lowered in place after the foaming mass is introduced into the female part. Thus, in the case of radomes, the lower mold is lined on the inside with polyester laminate, and placed under the upper mold similarly

Figure 3.2e. Contour check on trimmed part.

lined on the outside. These surfaces are roughened by light sand-blasting for improved adhesion. The foam ingredients are blended in an external bowl, etc., and introduced into the female mold at the proper time. The male mold is lowered until the proper thickness tolerance is obtained, and the foam is allowed to rise up the side between the two polyester laminates. The close tolerance finally obtained may be noted in the illustration. This method is also used in potting operations, where the blended foam ingredients are

Figure 3.2f. Completed dome coated with rain erosion-resistant material.

poured into and around the electronic components, and a bar is placed above to restrain the rising foam. The restrain pattern may be varied from a large overflow to fine air vents. Panels have been successfully made by this method.

The second method differs from the first in that the restrain pattern is placed before the pouring is done; and, hence, one must be able to pour through comparatively small openings. This is why it is often necessary to have a blended diisocyanate resin system that is quite fluid. This method has been used successfully for plane tabs and ailerons. In such cases, one-inch holes have been used. However, in filling thin panels and container walls, openings as small as one-quarter inch have been successfully used. These two general methods are basic and can be modified to fit all cases.

As is common to the general field of plastics, there is a paucity of physical data relative to the rigid foams discussed here. Most of the data have been obtained from core samples and, hence, may not be a realistic measure of the physical properties desired. Thus, it is best to use this data as an indication of what may be obtained, and to run the necessary tests on the final product. Other core sample data may then be used in conjunction with the above as a relative measure. The first interesting factor is that these foams are unicellular; that is, they are closed and non-connecting. This may be demonstrated by submerging samples of rigid foam in either an aqueous solution of a dye or a gasoline solution of a dye. No dye will be found to have penetrated the foam regardless of whether the samples are then cut wet or dry; it will only appear on the surface and where there is a disturbed (cut) layer of cells. Since the foams are highly cross-linked, solvents will have little effect on them.

In selecting a foam for present-day applications, electrical, mechanical or thermal properties must be taken into consideration. Electrically, radomes have been a highly successful application for foams, due to their low dielectric constants and low power losses. Thus, it is found that polyurethane is practically transparent to those electromagnetic waves which are used in radio and radar work.

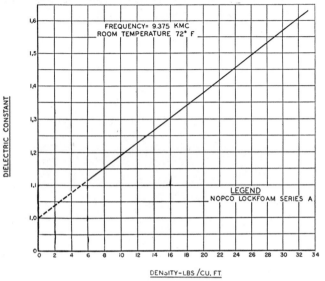

Figure 3.3. Dielectric constant vs density.

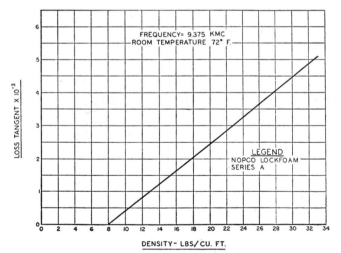

Figure 3.4. Loss tangent vs density.

Potting is also an important application. Here, a lightweight pour-in-place dielectric acts as a protection against vibrational damage and as a barrier to dampness, corrosion, and fungi.

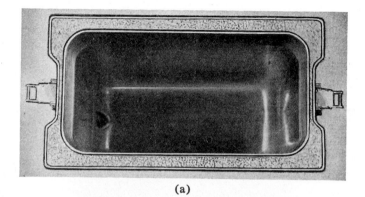

(a)

(b)

Figure 3.5. The potting operation.
(a) Foamed-in-place system for structural use.
(b) Foam being foamed-in-place for potting.

Figure 3.5. Continued.
(c) Cut specimen showing the finished product filled with foam.

The Germans demonstrated the good mechanical strengths obtainable with these foams. Figure 3.6 shows the mechanical strengths obtained at various temperatures for one commercial foam system.

Because of the high cross-branchings, these foams show excellent strengths at elevated temperatures. A temperature level of 160°F is the normal commercially accepted practice. There has been an increasing demand for temperatures up to 250°F and it is possible that temperatures up to 400°F may be desired. These temperature levels are quite reasonable, at the present stage of development. The mechanical properties of foams are used to advantage in reinforcing airplane components (where light-weight is a premium), such as doors, ailerons, tabs, etc. In addition, walls of various containers are made of a sandwich construction using foam cores. This type of structure has many uses because these foams are excellent heat insulators. The lower the density, the better the foam in this respect. The thermal conductivity is in the range of 0.2 Btu/hr/ft²/in./°F, which places it among the better heat insulators.

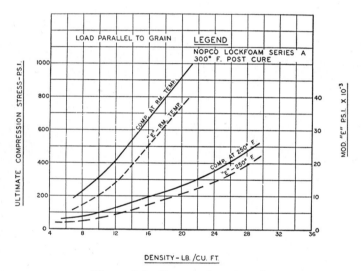

Figure 3.6. Compression strength.

Until recently, all of the above rigid foam formulations were mixed by batch methods, employing either hand-mixing or simple stirring equipment. This method of handling was a definite drawback for large-scale foam production. Several types of mechanical equipment are now available which automatically meter, mix and dispense foams in predetermined quantities. They are also designed to run either continuously or intermittently, with capacities ranging from 2 to 35 pounds per minute. Because of the range of viscosities of the resin, catalyst, and diisocyanate components, no single piece of equipment can be designed to handle all formulations. Therefore, it becomes necessary to select the machine which will be best suited for the formulation in question. There are presently three types of machines which will dispense formulations now available on the market. The use of mechanical devices has greatly increased the potential and immediate sale of foamed urethane products.

Figure 3.7. Cellular structure of rigid Lockfoam thermosetting foamed-in-place plastic used for plane ailerons.

After World War II, the Germans investigated the rigid polyurethanes further, and apparently worked out a technique based on mechanical, continuous mixing. Their principle of fast blending employs a catalyst (some tertiary amine) which promotes a quick reaction so that the partial reaction products bind the reaction mass together. Thus, in essence, three streams of reactants meet in a mixing chamber, and the foaming mass is delivered continuously to a cavity or a conveyor (for slab stock). The streams are:

1. Resin
2. Tolylene diisocyanate
3. Activator solution containing water, catalyst, emulsifier, cell modifiers, etc.

It will be noted that this is similar to their technique for flexible foam. Some variations are possible; the simplest is to pre-mix the activator solution and the resin. Many variations have been developed by American investigators. The most important one is built around the pre-reaction of part of the resin with all of the diisocyanate. This is a comparatively new development. The physical properties of these foams are expected to compare favorably with the previous ones if similar resins are employed. These are sometimes called partial (or quasi) prepolymer systems.

4. SEMI-RIGID FOAMS

As pointed out previously, if the number of branch points and the spacing between and within branch chains are varied in polyurethanes, we can obtain, theoretically, a continuous spectrum of rigidity ranging from very flexible to highly rigid. This is equally true of cellular polyurethanes. Rigid foams were discussed in Chapter 3; flexible foams will be discussed in Chapter 5. In between is a region which has not been precisely defined and which is referred to as that of semi-rigid foams. Since foams, in general, are of interest here only insofar as they are employed as physical entities, the semi-rigid foams may be characterized by their physical behavior, one phase of which may be illustrated by Figure 4.1.

Here, a rigid foam (14 pounds density) is contrasted to a semi-rigid foam (17 pounds density). A plot of stress-strain curves at both room temperature and 160°F is given. Ignoring the fact that the lower density rigidity is stronger at room temperature, it should be noted that the moduli of rigidity for the semi-rigid foam, as represented by the slopes of the curves, is about one-third that of the rigid. Hence, it is possible that a certain quantity of flexible foam characteristics is being displayed here. Elevation of the testing temperature accentuates this even more. At 160°F the semi-rigid foam cannot carry any load, whereas the rigid foam is affected relatively little. These factors, though not defining the foams, give an indication of how they may be expected to act in a mechanical sense. A better idea may be derived from later discussions of their main representative—castor oil-based foams and their properties.

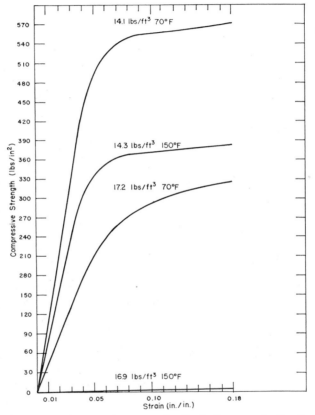

Figure 4.1. Compressive strength (lbs/in²) vs strain (in./in.).

A cheap hydroxyl-rich natural product with branch points, which has found application as a raw material for the preparation of polyurethanes, is castor oil. This vegetable oil can be described as the mixed glycerides of ricinoleic acid (85%) and oleic acid (15%). An idealization of the main fraction of this oil may be given as follows:

since ricinoleic acid is:

$$CH_3CH_2CH_2CH_2CH_2CH_2CH-CH_2CH=CHCH_2CH_2CH_2CH_2CH_2CH_2CH_2COOH$$
$$\underset{OH}{|}$$

The next large fraction would contain two hydroxyls per glyceride molecule. To utilize this raw material, it is necessary to pre-react it with diisocyanate because its replaceable hydrogens may be seen to be buried secondary hydroxyl groups of relatively low reactivity. The usual procedure is to react the castor oil with at least one mole of diisocyanate for each hydroxyl group, which is equivalent to replacing each hydroxyl with an isocyanate group. The products formed are called "prepolymers"; these have many uses. In making foams these prepolymers are reacted with an aqueous solution of catalyst. The water reacts with the free isocyanate groups, producing carbon dioxide gas and forming urea linkages which unite the molecules of the prepolymer into a single, huge molecule, which is the foam.

The cellular polyurethane systems developed by DuPont are based on castor oil formulations; these may be found outlined in their U.S.P. 2,787,601. These foams are essentially of the open, semi-rigid type, and are capable of being produced in a density range of 2 to 20 pounds. It should be pointed out that prepolymer systems which use mainly water to form good semi-rigid foam need not be made only from castor oil. More recently, National Aniline has been studying the use of castor oil for low-density foams and has suggested a formulation which may be used to illustrate the processing of castor oil and the resulting prepolymer.

Thirty to fifty grams of finely divided powdered silica is mixed with 1300 grams of tolylene diisocyanate (80/20 isomer ratio). To this slurry, 1800 grams of a good grade of castor oil is added, with constant agitation. The temperature may reach 185°F; it is then raised to 275°F and kept there for one hour, and the product is allowed to cool. This prepolymer should have a viscosity range of 40,000 to 70,000 centipoises at room temperature for the best foaming results. The silica is used to counteract possible shrinkage of the final foam. The quantity depends on the fineness of the filler; the finer this is, the less used. In order to foam this, it is necessary to add catalysts to activate the reaction with water. The activator solution is:

Water	100	parts
Dimethyl ethanol amine	45	parts
Non-anionic emulsifier	65	parts

and it is used in the ratio of 7.5 parts to 100 parts of prepolymer. The two are agitated together vigorously at room temperature for 10 to 20 seconds and then poured into the cavity or mold. After 24 hours, the foam will have self-cured sufficiently to develop fully its physical properties.

The castor oil-based foams are presently being made and used in large quantities. Most of the formulations and quantities are based on the duPont systems, where the viscosity of the prepolymer is in the range of 10,000 to 20,000 centipoises. Hence, a study of their basic physical properties (as given in their HR-1 Report) would help one to understand semi-rigid foams and to find proper applications for them. It should be pointed out that these foams are somewhat thermoplastic; they will not melt, but will become noticeably softer with moderate increases in temperature. Figures 4.2 and 4.3 show how these foams lose their load-bearing abilities with small increases in temperature (note change in scale).

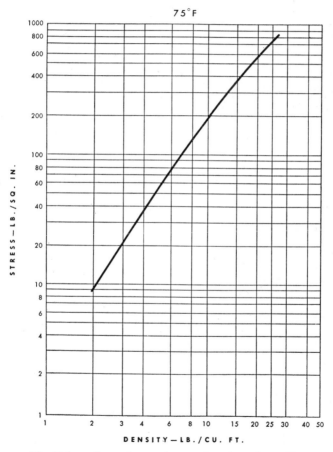

Figure 4.2. Polyurethane foam compressive strength at 50 per cent deflection. (*Figures 4.2-4.8 courtesy E. I. du Pont de Nemours & Co., Inc.*)

In spite of this, these foams will not distort under their own weight below 200°F and, hence, can be used at higher temperatures. However, at the same time, any possible application where severe bearing requirements have to be met at these elevated temperatures must be carefully scrutinized.

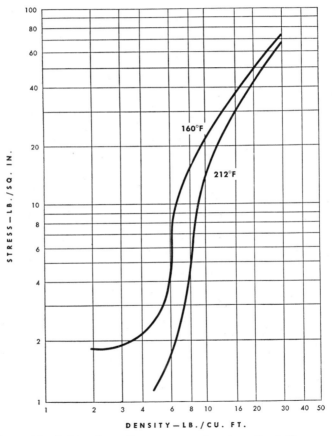

Figure 4.3. Polyurethane foam compressive strength at 50 per cent deflection at elevated temperatures.

In contrast to rigid foams, where the elastic limit is reached much before or, on the extreme, near the 10 per cent deformation point in compression studies, these foams are

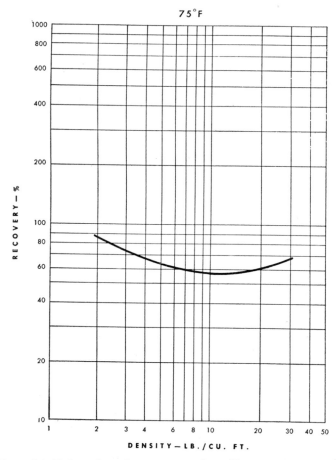

Figure 4.4. Polyurethane foam recovery from 50 per cent compressive deflection.

studied in compressive strengths up to 50 per cent (Figures
4.2 and 4.3) and even 75 per cent. Here, too, a high
recovery is found after this high deformation, as illustrated
in Figures 4.4 and 4.5.

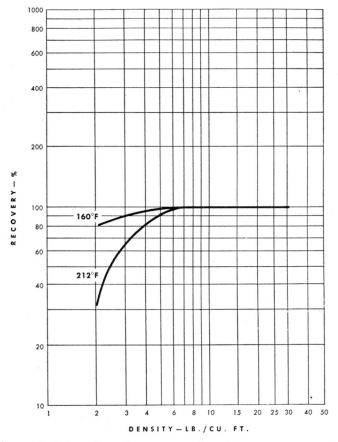

Figure 4.5. Polyurethane foam recovery from 50 per cent compressive
deflection at elevated temperatures.

These plots tend to confirm the concept of inherent flexibility in semi-rigid foams. The improved recovery at elevated temperatures (Figure 4.5) supports this idea of flexibility more strongly. It is interesting to note that the

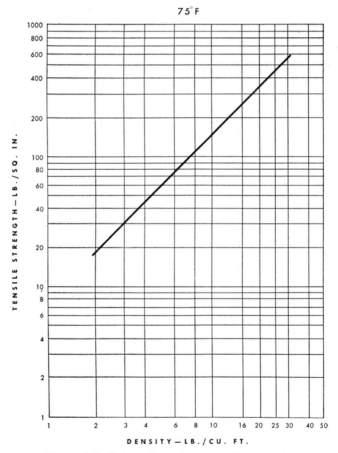

Figure 4.6. Polyurethane foam tensile strength.

tensile strength shows a similar temperature effect, as does compressive strength. Thus, Figure 4.6, at room temperature, and Figure 4.7, at elevated temperatures, show data roughly equivalent to those of Figures 4.2 and 4.3.

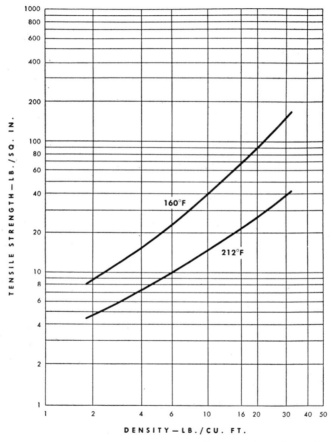

Figure 4.7. Polyurethane foam tensile strength at elevated temperatures.

It is hoped that these physical properties will give a concept of semi-rigid foams.

One of the outstanding advantages of castor oil-based foams is the excellent bond formed between the foamed-in-place foam and the various materials used to form cavities.

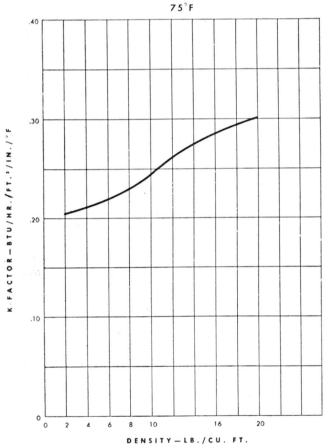

Figure 4.8. Polyurethane foam thermal conductivity.

TABLE 4.1. BOND STRENGTHS OF POLYURETHANE FOAMS

Foam Density, lb/cu ft	2	5	10	20
Bond Strength, psi				
To aluminum	10	27	56	158
To glass	9	25	50	142
To steel	12	29	62	146
To wood	17	29	62	170

All that is required to produce these bond strengths is simple degreasing by a solvent rinse; no primer or special surface preparation is required. Table 4.1 compared to Figure 4.6 shows that, although these values are less than the tensile strength of the foam, they are roughly of the same order. Perhaps the largest use of these foams has been in the field of insulation. Here, the excellent K factor exhibited by these products, together with their comparatively low cost, forecasts a larger potential in this field. Figure 4.8 shows the low-heat conductivity and the advantage of low density.

It may be noted here that only small variations in the K factor have been reported in the temperature range of 75 to 200°F. A good insulation must be one which is not affected by moisture; the presence of water in an insulation material will cause it to lose its insulation qualities. Since semi-rigid foams are composed of open cells, water can be mechanically absorbed (see Table 4.2).

TABLE 4.2. WATER ABSORPTION—POUNDS OF WATER
PER CUBIC FOOT

Foam Density	2	4	16	20
25 Days in water (total immersion)	24.56	22.8	4.0	2.0
120 Hours at 50% relative humidity	0.006	0.027	0.067	0.084
120 Hours at 98% relative humidity	0.38	0.386	0.359	0.56

Therefore in practical use the surface of these foams must be protected from contact with water by the application of coatings, etc. The foams are hydrophobic and, hence, will not tend to absorb moisture from the air. Only lack of direct contact with liquid water is necessary in foam applications.

In contrast to rigid foams, solvents will soften semi-rigid foams and even swell them to some degree. They may be weaker in this state, but on removal of the solvents, they regain their original strengths. Also, whereas rigid foams will burn readily, unless self-snuffing additives are used, semi-rigid foams will burn in the presence of a flame, but are self-extinguishable upon the removal of the flame. The self-snuffing characteristics may be improved by adding chlorinated hydrocarbon, phosphates, borates, silicates, etc. The inherent self-snuffing properties are apparently caused by localized melting which quenches the flame. This would not be possible with the much higher branched rigid foams.

Since the viscosity of the prepolymers made by the duPont procedures is in the range of 10,000 to 20,000 cp at room temperature, they are capable of being mechanically mixed for either intermittent or continuous foaming with the equipment available at present. This is especially true if the piece of equipment is equipped with heat exchangers. Because of their comparatively low viscosities, these prepolymers can also be sprayed. The DeVilbiss Company has developed a spray gun (P-JGC-504) which is being used to spray the equivalent of a two-pound density foam of this type. It is claimed that ⅛ inch to over a 2 inch thickness has been successfully sprayed. Heaters are essential as auxiliary equipment; these are necessary to reduce the initial viscosity of the prepolymer to a sprayable consistency. This would suggest the possibility of producing acoustic insulation by spraying. For this purpose, the lowest density foam is best, perhaps in part, because of its higher percentage of open cells (see Table 4.2). Table 4.3 illustrates this clearly.

TABLE 4.3. SOUND ABSORPTION COEFFICIENTS

Density, lb/cu ft	2	6	10
250 cycles/sec.	0.79	0.20	0.22
500 cycles/sec.	0.99	0.22	0.22
1000 cycles/sec.	0.97	0.20	0.31

Figures 4.9a-f. Foam-in-place technique for insulating a T-joint.

Figure 4.9a. A T-joint.

It must be emphasized that viscosity considerations are mainly responsible for the ease with which these prepolymers can be mechanically foamed.

As already indicated, perhaps the most important use of the castor oil-based foams is in the field of insulation. Here, the feature of being able to foam-in-place cuts down the need for large inventories of prefabricated forms and the large handling cost of cutting and fashioning preformed slabs to fit various shapes and cavities. An excellent example of this is the application of insulation to T joints. Figures 4.9a through f show how a simple form is placed around a joint, with the aid of masking tape, and how the foam blend is poured around it. The foam rises slowly and fills the form which is removed as soon as the foam loses its tack.

Figure 4.9b. T-joint with plastic mold taped into place.

These prepolymers do not exert much pressure in foaming in contrast to the usual rigid foams which require strong jigs to restrain the mold. The low density foam as used here is a slow riser; however, the higher density castor oil-based prepolymer can be made to foam at faster rates. In fact, in some formulations, the catalyst can be altered to produce foams which rise faster and are stronger than those shown in Figures 4.9a-f.

Figure 4.9c. Start of addition of isocyanate blend.

In addition to their insulation properties, these prepolymers are used to fill spaces where none or small amounts of load-bearing requirements are expected. Thus, an interesting application is filling the space between a processing vessel and the floor, as shown in Figure 4.10. A more common practice is the filling of panels for structural and insulation applications. With the adoption of mechanical mixing, more and more of these panels are being filled for use in homes, truck bodies, etc. Various density foams are used.

Figure 4.9d.   End of pour.

It has recently been suggested that low density semi-rigid foams would make a good packaging material. Thus, a layer of foam could be foamed in place around an object placed in a shipping container. Two general considerations are applied: (1) the foam may be used to distribute the load during shipment and avoid breakage at a weak point,

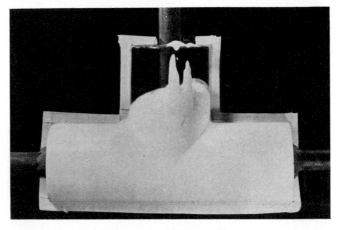

Figure 4.9e. Foam rise.

Figure 4.9f. Final foam with mold removed.

or (2) it may be used for what is called a "one-shot" shipping application. Thus, in a single drop, such as in an airplane drop, the semi-rigid foam will be crushed, being the weakest spot, and in crushing will absorb the shock of

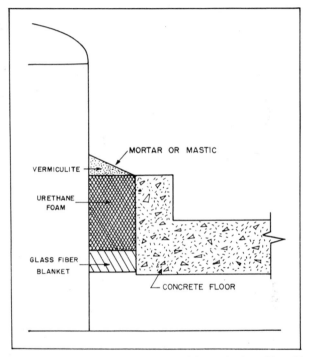

Figure 4.10. Cross-section showing position of glass fiber blanket, foamed urethane, vermiculite "soft" concrete, and hard mortar finish coat. (*Courtesy Chemical Processing.*)

the fall. Each packaging application must be carefully analyzed to determine what type of packaging physicals are required. Foams have a definite place in this field.

Although we have discussed the castor oil-based prepolymer as the only semi-rigid formulation on the market, others may be available soon. In the case of some of the quasi-prepolymers, the tendency is to use low viscosity oils in order to obtain ease of handling. In most cases, it must be recognized that this is done at the sacrifice of heat distortion qualities by lowering the quantity of cross-branching, which leads to a semi-rigid foam.

5. FLEXIBLE FOAMS

To the general public, as well as to many, if not most, of the technical workers in the plastic field, the word "polyurethane" has the connotation of flexible foams. For both groups, the main contact with polyurethanes is only through these flexible foams. Despite the fact that these materials are comparatively new, they have found their way into the home and industry for many uses. In Germany, where the economic structure is a strong determining factor, they monopolize the flexible foam field. These materials have many uses there that do not appear to be feasible as yet in this country. Thus, we find brushes of many types, such as tooth brushes, cleaning brushes, clothing brushes, etc. (Figure 5.1) made of flexible polyurethane. Many unusual fabrications are also found, one of which is an eggholder used even during the boiling process. In America, these materials are the largest consumers of our diisocyanate production, with the result that they have been making great inroads into the flexible foam market. In time, it is expected that the price structure for flexible foams will become more and more favorable over their rivals. In recent years, the diisocyanates and the polyhydroxyl-base materials have shown substantial decreases in prices, and, hence, should make even greater inroads in the future.

As with the other polyurethanes, these flexible foams show a wide variation of properties. Figures 5.2 and 5.3

show foams at two different density levels which have widely different load-bearing characteristics. Figure 5.2 is representative of four 6-pound density foams which vary in handling from a firm foam (top) to a very soft one (bottom). In fact, the soft one can be balled up by handling, and will slowly return to shape in a period of minutes. Figure 5.3 shows similar variation at a 2-pound density level, with less of a range. Thus, it can be seen that many

(*Courtesy Mobay Chemical Co.*)

Figure 5.1. Some brushes made of flexible polyurethane.

load-bearing characteristics may be obtained within a given density level. Another factor, which may be altered within a given density level, is the shape of the stress-strain curve which affects the energy absorption character, crustiness, etc. Figure 5.4 shows the stress-strain curves of a polyester-based foam (bottom) and a polyether-based foam (top) at a 2-pound density; the former has less resiliency (or greater energy absorption). These graphs show the versatility of the flexible foam formulations available at present, and point out their many potential uses.

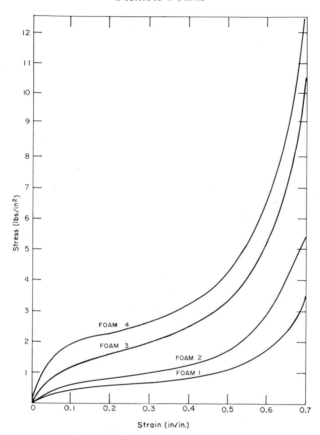

Figure 5.2. Stress-strain curves showing the first loading for four poured-in-place flexible foams.

Some flexible polyurethane foams were available in the United States prior to the entrance of Mobay into this field. However, the big impetus, commercially speaking, came from the licensing of the Mobay know-how. Some material had been imported from Germany and the European licensees of Bayer, but production in this country was not

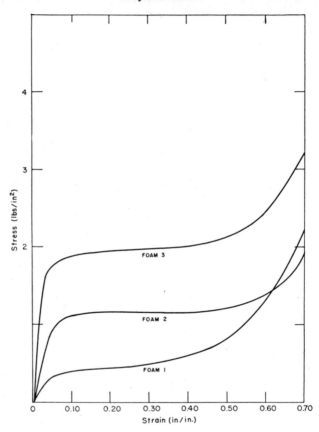

Figure 5.3. Stress-strain curves showing the first loading for three
2 lb/ft³ slab stock.

significant. The Mobay process uses polyester resins of their
own production in the so-called "one-shot" system. Other
polyester suppliers have developed similar resins and have,
in conjunction with diisocyanate producers, developed other
one-shot systems, as well as systems which depend on both

actual and potential prepolymers. (The latter expression will be explained later.) All of these foams are based on polyester resins. duPont has revealed that "Teracol," a polybutylene ether, can be used as the polyhydroxy compound instead of polyester resins to make flexible foams with improved aging characteristics and better resiliency. However, the price of this base chemical is considered too high for extensive commercial exploitation. Lately, other polyethers of much lower cost have shown promise and are

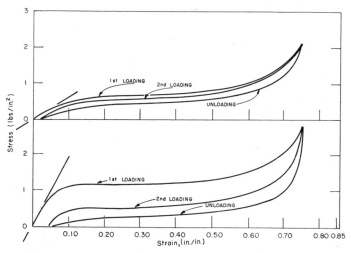

Figure 5.4. Stress-strain curves for polyester-based foams.

being investigated. The lower cost of the polyethers, compared to the polyesters, may lower the price of the final foam provided the extra steps of producing the necessary true prepolymers and foaming them do not add to the costs. To round out this terse history, it should be pointed out that Mobay, through one of its parent companies, Farbenfabriken Bayer Aktiengesellschaft, has obtained patent rights in this country to their process for the manufacture of polyurethane. This patent (U.S.P. 2,764,565, issued September 25, 1956) may be consulted for basic processes and apparatus.

In order to understand the general methods of producing flexible foam, a formulation obtained from the above patent will be discussed. For the moment the mechanical means of the patent will be ignored. One hundred parts, by volume, of a polyester of the following composition:

> 16 moles—adipic acid
> 16 moles—diethylene glycol
> 1 mole —trimethylol propane

was reacted with 47 parts by volume of tolylene diisocyanate in the presence of 10 parts by volume of an activator mixture of the following composition:

> 3   —adipic acid ester of N-diethyl aminoethanol
> 1   —ammonium oleate
> 1.5—sulphonated castor oil
> 1.5—water
> 0.5—paraffin oil

This produced a flexible foam of 2.2 pounds per cubic foot density. The technique involved here is called the "one-shot" method. All ingredients are mixed at one time with no pre-reacting. It should be noted that the activator mixture composition is a comparatively complex one. There are present in it components, which are cell-size regulators, cross-linking agents, catalysts and emulsifiers to keep the activator mixtures homogeneous. As indicated in Chapter 3, the catalyst enables the reaction mass to become homogeneous quickly, aiding the compatability of the reactants so that the urethane reaction proceeds smoothly while the gas from the water reaction is being trapped. In actual practice, this process is not suitable for manual handling, but requires continuous mechanical processes. At most, 100 grams or so of these formulations can be blended by hand stirring.

The mechanical means available and the preference of the operator have influenced the manner in which the ingredients are combined. The simplest variation in this method is to mix together the resin with water and the other activator solution components before adding the diisocyanate. Many operators think that they can improve this process by first mixing the resin and diisocyanate (potential prepolymer), and by allowing the mixture to stand at room temperature for a period of an hour or so before adding the activator solution. It must be realized, by again referring to Figure 2.3, (p. 19), that the reaction between the resin and diisocyanate does not proceed very far under these conditions; hence, it is called a "potential prepolymer." In fact, if this reaction is forced toward substantial completion to form a true prepolymer, the foam conditions must be radically altered. In addition, a method that falls in between the above two may be used in which one-half of the resin is mixed with all the tolylene diisocyanate, and all the activator solution is mixed with the other half of the resin. Finally, the two mixtures are blended. Each method has its exponents who base their preference on what they believe to be ease of handling and better foam (structurally and physically).

At the present time, most of the polyurethane flexible foam is based on diethylene glycol-adipic acid polyesters. The following physical characteristics are typical of these foams.

TABLE 5.1

Density, lb/ft^3	2.2
Compression-load-deflection, lb/in^2 (25%)	0.59
(50%)	0.73
(75%)	2.03
Tear strength (Block Method), lb/in	3.4
Tensile strength, lb/in^2	19.5
Tensile elongation, %	430
Compression-set, %	8.4
Cell size, cells/in.	60

Simple variations in the above polyester formulation can affect the load-bearing capacity without any appreciable change in density. Thus, changes in the tolylene diisocyanate isomer ratios (range is from 100%—2.4 to 65%—2.4 with 35%—2.6) are found to have this effect. Generally, the lower the 2,4-isomer percentage, the stiffer the foam, but the softest foams are found in the range of 76 to 81 per cent. Similarly, other physical properties have been affected. Other ingredients, such as those found in activator solutions, also have an effect. The type of emulsifier, catalyst, etc., has been noted to show similar effects. Of course, similar differences could be produced in the foam by altering the polyester by varying triol, etc., but this is not a common practice. The usual procedure is to vary the formulation. An advantage that the foam polyurethanes have over foam rubber is their excellent resistance to oxidation. However, they have the disadvantage of being liable to hydrolysis. This will be discussed in more detail later with respect to the way in which it happens and how it may be alleviated. However, in connection with the one-shot polyester method of preparing flexible polyurethanes, it is possible to relate this factor to the quantity of tolylene diisocyanate used in the formulation.

Many flexible formulations suggested by raw material suppliers other than Mobay are derived from the following generalized formulation:

Tolylene diisocyanate 80/20—to be adjusted to requirements
Polyester resin—(similar to previous)
Dispersing agent (nonionic and anionic)
Water
Catalysts (methyl morpholine, diethylethanolamine, etc.)

The ingredients are usually calculated on the basis of 100 parts of resin; the quantities of the last three ingredients depend on the density and cell structure desired. It is possible to obtain lower density foams more easily by using less than the theoretical amount of diisocyanate necessary to combine with the other ingredients in the formulation. However, when this is done, the foam is less resistant to hydrolysis (aging). In fact, if about 60 to 70 per cent of theory is employed, the foam will soften and deteriorate relatively fast under normal room conditions. To detect the poorer quality, a foam having a tolylene diisocyanate content between this range and 100 per cent would require an accelerated test. In general, at least 100 per cent should be used, and preferably 5 to 10 per cent excess. Raising the excess above this range tends to introduce a quality of harshness into the foams, accompanied by brittleness.

As pointed out above, in order to make foam by this method, a means of mechanical metering, mixing and dispensing is required. Mobay Chemical Company holds the patent rights to a process for accomplishing this. They claim a process in which a polymeric material, containing free hydroxyl groups, a polyisocyanate and an activator mixture, which influences the reaction leading to the formation of the porous polyurethane plastics, are brought together in an enclosed mixing zone in such a manner that at least one of the last two mentioned components is injected into said mixing zone intermittently at high frequency, at a pressure substantially higher than that prevailing in the mixing zone. All of the components are thereby admixed, and the resultant mixture is discharged in the liquid state and crosslinked. Several of the pieces of the mechanical equipment shown in their patent will be described. The apparatus shown in Figure 5.5 is suggested for production of the above foam.

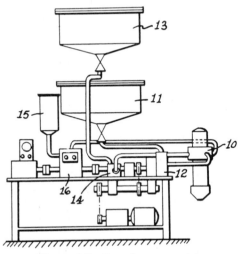

Figure 5.5. Foaming apparatus.

According to Example 2 of this patent, the polyester, held at a temperature of 22°C, is continuously fed from the storage tank (11) into the reaction or mixing device (10) by means of the pump (12) and, simultaneously but separately, the polyisocyanate, held at a temperature of 18°C, is injected into the reaction or mixing device (10) from the storage tank (13) intermittently by means of the pump (14) and an activator from the storage tank (15) intermittently, by means of the pump (16). The polyester is fed continuously at the rate of 4 liters per minute, while the diisocyanate is fed at the rate of 2 liters per minute, being injected at 9,000 pulses per minute. The activator solution is added at the rate of 0.4 liters per minute, intermittently, at 3,000 injections per minute.

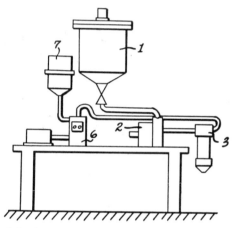

Figure 5.6. Apparatus for foaming, pumping and mixing.

Figure 5.6 shows another apparatus for storing, pumping and mixing the several components. Tank (1) is charged with a mixture of polyester and polyisocyanate. This mixture is continuously pumped by the gear pump (2), to the reaction or mixing device (3). Tank (7) is charged with the activator solution which is pumped intermittently by the injection pump (6) to the reaction or mixing device (3). Three embodiments of a mixing device are shown in Figures 5.7, 5.8 and 5.9. The device shown in Figure 5.7 contains

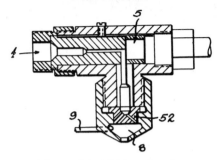

Figure 5.7. Mixing chamber.

a feed pipe (5), in which the polyester-polyisocyanate mixture is continuously pumped. An injection nozzle (4) is provided for intermittently injecting the activator component into the continuously flowing polyester-polyisocyanate mixture. The activator component is injected countercurrently

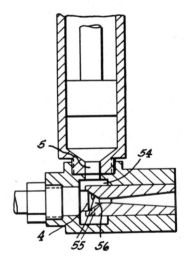

Figure 5.8. Mixing chamber.

into the other components. After injection, the resulting mixture is forced through the nozzle plate (52) into the mixing chamber (8) into which a stream of compressed air is introduced through a tangentially disposed air pipe (9). Intense mixing of the components is accomplished by this procedure. Figure 5.8 shows the device used to inject the activator component into the other two components transversely to their flow. First, the polyester-polyisocyanate mixture enters the ring chamber (54), via the feed pipe (5). The mixture is then forced through slots (55) into the mix-

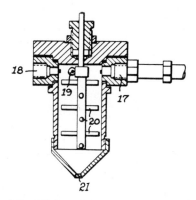

Figure 5.9. Mixing chamber employing a stirrer.

ing chamber (56), where it is mixed intensely with the activator component, which has been intermittently injected through the nozzle (4). In this embodiment, no secondary mixing (e.g., by air or mechanical means) is employed. Figure 5.9 illustrates a mixing chamber employing a stirrer (20). The three components are admitted to the chamber via nozzles (17), (18) and (19). The resulting mixture leaves through outlet (21).

When the liquid foaming mixture is discharged from the

mixer, it is necessary to have some means of laying the foam down to produce good slabs. The best solution to date has been to have the molds move continuously past the mixing head, while the mixing head moves transversely over the width of the mold. (Figures 5.10a and 5.10b)

(*Courtesy Mobay Chemical Co.*)

Figure 5.10a. A piece of specially designed foam-producing machinery, the mixing head moves across the mold, depositing liquid layer which swells into a 10-inch foam.

The Figures, which are self-explanatory, are typical of this operation. At this point, the loaves may be allowed to set and self-cure, or be placed into curing ovens. Many formulations require curing in order to obtain good compression-set qualities. Compression-set is the measure of how a foam is expected to pack down in use. The industry uses an accelerated test to obtain a relative rating for a given foam. The recovery of a sample which has been subjected to a

(*Courtesy Mobay Chemical Co.*)

Figure 5.10b. Before the six-foot-long mold has finished making its run, the foaming action is completed at the far end.

compression of one-half its height for 22 hours at 158°F is determined. Recovery of at least 90 per cent of its original height after one-half hour at room temperature is usually considered good.

(*Courtesy Mobay Chemical Co.*)

Figure 5.11. After curing, the 10-inch-thick block, 40 inches wide
and 6 feet long, is easily taken from the mold.

After the foam slab is produced, it has to be cut into
usable forms. The flexible urethanes lend themselves to easy
splitting and cutting. Equipment is available commercially
which can be used to produce sheets of foams as thin as
3/32 inch with high uniformity. Figure 5.12 shows a piece
of equipment which can be used with additional conveyors
to produce long sheets. These sheets can then be cut into
various forms similarly to cloth in layers, as shown in Fig-

ure 5.13. It is often possible to die-cut sheets of foam. Formulations which will give flexible urethane foams of clickable grades are also available. The above operations, and the fact that it is possible to adhere foam to itself and to heat-seal it, combined with its excellent physical properties, have enabled foam products to find manifold uses in the household.

(*Courtesy The Fall Engineering & Machine Co.*)

Figure 5.12. Campbell conveyorized slab leveling and splitting machine.

These foams are highly resistant to solvents and detergents. Figure 5.14 shows examples of various products used in cleaning and decorating. The production of sponges is so large that special sponge cutting equipment has become available. The machine shown in Figure 5.15 is capable of producing several different sizes of sponges, such as 2″ x 2″, 3″ x 5″, and 4″ x 6″, with various thickness and/or several ply. One apparent drawback to these sponges is that they are hydrophobic and do not wipe dry; however, since they

(*Courtesy Mobay Chemical Co.*)

Figure 5.13. Sheets of foam being die-cut.

can tolerate much handling without tearing, do not harden on drying, and withstand detergent solutions and solvents, a large market has been opened up for them. Another item for which increased production is anticipated is rug underlays. There is some controversy, however, whether the foam should be adhered to the rug or not. Another important point concerns the physical properties of the foam. A formulation must have the proper elongation, good tear strength and shear resistance to perform properly; just any foam will not do, and a performance test of some sort should be made on a given foam before it is sold. An added advantage to the use of foam as underlays is their non-skid property.

However, to enable a rug to be laid conveniently upon foam (to be kicked down), the upper surface of the foam should be treated with some coating or material to overcome any friction (Figure 5.16).

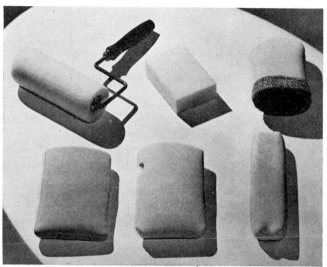

(*Courtesy Mobay Chemical Co.*)

Figure 5.14. Urethane foams for household applications. Strong, lightweight, flexible urethane foams made from isocyanates and polyesters supplied by Mobay Chemical Company can be used for a variety of household applications. The cleanability of urethane foam, plus its resistance to soaps, detergents and all solvents, makes it useful for paint rollers, sponges, scrubbing pads (top); polishing pads, bath mitts, and floor brushes (bottom).

Many novelty uses have been found for these foams, and the fact that they are available in various colors is important. Color is introduced during the foaming process in the form of pigments. They may be either water dispersed or dispersible, and, hence added in the activator solution or oil-dispersed and introduced via the resin stream. The foams are cut, clicked, sewed, adhered and heat-sealed to form caps, dolls, various types of slippers, ironing-board pads,

(*Courtesy The Fall Engineering & Machine Co.*)

Figure 5.15. 24-inch Rudmar block cutter.

clothes hanger pads, glass coasters and absorbent sleeves, etc. Shoulder pads are a large use. Here, resistance to cleaning fluid is a determining factor. An important property of the urethane foams is their excellent heat insulation. Because of this, a tremendous market potential has been predicted for interlinings. It is expected that within three years 15,000,000 square yards will be sold annually. When it is found that ⅛ inch thickness of foam is equivalent to 11 to 16 ounces of wool batting, and that it weighs only 2 to 3 ounces per square yard, about one-fifth the bulk of competitive materials, this prediction does not appear too optimistic. It

(*Courtesy Mobay Chemical Co.*)

Figure 5.16. Foam used as underlay for rug.

must also be remembered that foam can be handled as one would handle fabric in cutting and sewing operations. Foam excels in the latter operation because of its good tear strength. There are other handling operations in which these foams can be used. Thus, Figures 5.17 and 5.18 show how foam is stapled and tacked without any protective coverings.

Polyurethane foams made from adipic acid polyesters have been suggested and used as cushioning materials; however, it has been found that these foams have too much creep and tend to bottom. Cushions will show continuous sag under load and will return too slowly when the load is removed, leaving a noticeable depression. This is due to the large plateau, as shown in Figure 5.4, bottom, and also

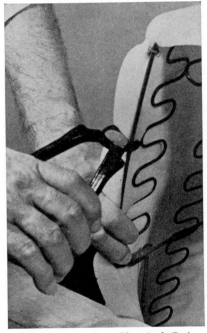

(*Courtesy Mobay Chemical Co.*)

Figure 5.17. Foam being stapled.

the large difference between first and second loading curves. These features are of importance for many types of packages where shock can be overcome by the creep or energy absorption. This will be covered more fully in the discussion on the new types of flexible polyurethanes, namely, those made from polyether. In the case of the above polyester-based foams, various methods of cutting and adhering the resultant shapes together were tried as the means of overcoming this disadvantage, but the present status of this is not too clear. In one of the methods of cutting hot wires are

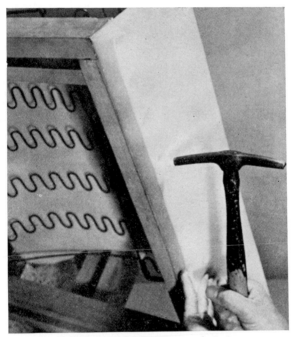

(*Courtesy Mobay Chemical Co.*)

Figure 5.18. Foam being tacked.

used. (See Figure 5.19 for some of the results possible with this type of cutting.) The lower potential price and higher resiliency exhibited by polyether-based foams have tended to push the polyester-based foams out of this field.

Recently, two raw materials have been suggested as replacements for adipic acid in polyesters, namely, caprolac-

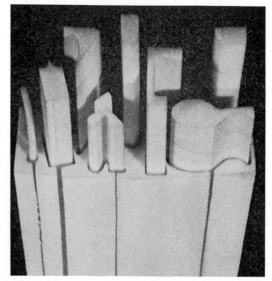

(*Courtesy Mobay Chemical Co.*)

Figure 5.19.   Polyester-based foams cut by means of hot wires.

tone and its alkyl derivatives, and dimer acids. Caprolactone is the inner ester of epsilon hydroxy hexanoic acid
and reacts ideally as HO——————COOH; hence, it can be
reacted by itself in the presence of a small amount of diol
or triol to form hydroxyl-rich polyesters suitable as raw
materials for polyurethanes in place of the above mentioned
diethylene glycol adipates. This lactone and its alkyl substituted lactones are obtained by treatment of certain frac-
tions obtained from coal tar and coal hydrogenation
operations.* What is most interesting is that flexible polyurethane foams which exhibited a great diversity of stress-

---

* For details, it is suggested reference be made to the original
papers given at the Symposium on Isocyanate Polymers at Atlantic
City, September 1956.

strain curves both in magnitude and in configuration were produced from these lactone polyesters. Thus, it is possible to produce foams resembling long plateau polyesters to those resembling polyethers. Furthermore, as shown in Figure 5.20, excellent low temperature performance is demonstrated by these polyurethanes.

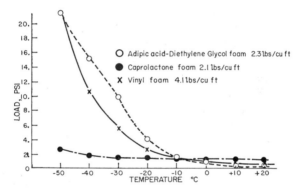

Figure 5.20. Compression modulus of foams versus temperature—25 per cent deflection.

The second raw material is dimer acids. These are produced when two molecules of linoleic acid are combined, usually in the presence of alkali, to form dibasic acids contaminated with some tribasic acids and monomers. An idealized structure of this raw material is:

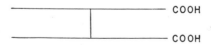

This chemical is used as a substitute for adipic acid in polyesters. The presence of the large alkyl chains radically affects the type of polyurethane foam obtained. Flexible foams based on the dimer acids are far more resistant to hydrolytic agents than those based on adipic acid. Furthermore, the foams exhibit higher resiliency and less plateau. One series of foams of this type demonstrated a strong dependence of load-bearing quality upon density so that the higher the density, the higher the load-bearing. This reported high dependence is not usual for polyurethanes.

One of the big advantages that flexible polyurethanes have over foam rubber is their inertness to oxidation. However, a possible shortcoming is their resistance to hydrolytic agents. A properly compounded polyurethane, based on polyester (using enough tolylene diisocyanate), can be used successfully in many operations where hydrolytic agents are present, as can be seen by merely looking at the list of applications— sponges, brushes, etc.). However, it is not possible, at the present, to forecast how long, under given conditions, a foam will retain its physical properties. It is only possible at present to give an idea of the relative efficiencies among various foams. It should be mentioned that, at present, there is no real agreement on the proper accelerated aging test, but that work is being done on it by round robins in the SPI.

Certain data have been obtained from testing adipic acid-based polyurethane foams which may be used to illustrate the present status for these flexibles. It has been revealed by duPont personnel that the hydrolytic action is at the urethane link, not the polyester. This indicates that the hydrophobic qualities of the foam would be the determining factor. This is shown in the case of dimer-acid foams. Figure 5.21 shows how foams of adipic acid polyesters lose their ability to withstand aging when excess water is used, again indicating that unreacted OH's, etc., are present which act as hydrophilic centers.

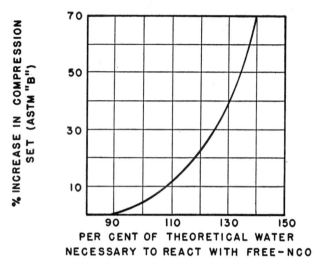

Figure 5.21. Effect of water concentration on the hydrolytic stability of polyester foams (aged 16 hours at 195°F and 100 per cent R.H.)

This is emphasized by the fact that foam made from a prepolymer is less strongly affected. Other experiments indicate a similar picture, two of which may be mentioned. One is that, if the acid number of the polyester is comparatively high (about 10) aging is poorer. Here, the amide link is at fault. If the tolylene diisocyanate ratio remains constant, but the total water content is increased, the aging is improved. It should be noted that these tests are run at 100 per cent relative humidity and, in most cases, at 195°F. Temperature would have an effect, as may be seen in Figure 5.22, which indicates the ordinary dependence on temperature found in most chemical reactions. The aging studies have given relative data; absolute data will depend on more experimentation and time-consuming studies under actual operating conditions.

The largest market anticipated for flexible polyurethanes is in the cushioning field (also, to a lesser degree, in the allied field of packaging). Figure 5.23 shows how many places foam can be used in an ordinary sofa. The big drawback to adipic acid polyester-based foam is its bad creep. DuPont developed a foam system based on a polyalkylene ether, called "Teracol," which showed much less creep.

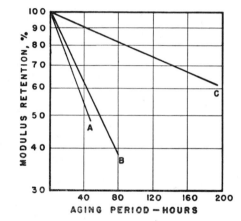

Figure 5.22. Change in modulus of polyester foams with aging at 100 per cent relative humidity.

A — 212°F	K = .0164/hr	
B — 195°F	K = .0122/hr	$K = \dfrac{2.303}{\text{Time}}\left(\text{Log}\ \dfrac{100}{\%\ \text{Retention}}\right)$
C — 158°F	K = .00251/hr	

Foamed rubber is used as the criterion in the cushioning field. We must remember that foamed rubber has been on the market for some time, and many people know what to expect when it is used. However, this may not be the true comfort desideratum. Comfort is a combination of physical and psychological factors. Merely approximating the stress-strain curve of foam rubber may not be enough. All of the sections of the sofa shown in Figure 5.23 do not require the same type of foam. The seat may require extra resiliency, but the back does not. Perhaps, here, more softness or creep

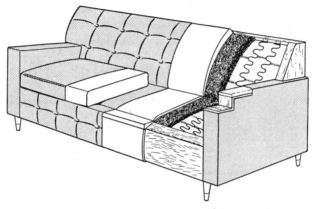

Figure 5.23. Cross-section of sofa showing use of foam.

is desired. Excessive creep is bad, but many applications require some creep. Until quite recently, "Teracol"-based foam was the only flexible foam available that could be used

TABLE 5.2. STRAIN DECAY PROPERTIES OF URETHANE FOAM

Material	Orig. Height at 25% Deflection, (In.)	Height After 1 Min. Dwell, (In.)	Orig. Height at 50% Deflection, (In.)	Height After 1 Min. Dwell, (In.)
Urethane foam, uncompounded polyester	0.75	0.62	0.50	0.40
Urethane foam, polyether resin	0.75	0.72	0.50	0.47
Urethane foam, "Teracol" resin	0.75	0.72	0.50	0.47
Natural rubber foam	0.75	0.73	0.50	0.48

successfully as an over-all material in the cushioning field. It had the extra resiliency necessary without the bad creep of the usual polyester-based flexible polyurethanes. In addition, it had better aging characteristics. However, the relatively high price of this polyalkylene ether was a drawback.

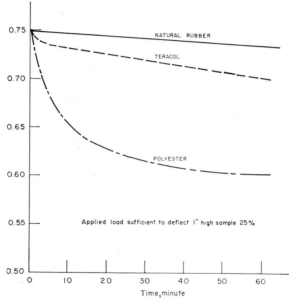

Figure 5.24. Strain decay properties.

Recently, several groups of polyethers have been studied as possible substitutes, with good results. These polyethers are either polypropylene glycols (Carbon and Carbide, and Dow), or mixed polypropylene-polyethylene glycols, such as "Ucons" (Carbon and Carbide) and "Pluronics" (Wyandotte). In addition, derivatives of these have been suggested. These products show an excellent potential for cushioning.

(See creep data in Table 5.2). Because of the possibilities of varying stress-strain without changes in density, it is possible to vary the load-bearing of a given cushion without too much trouble. These cushions appear to eliminate the necessity of coring and expensive molds. According to a large segment of the industry, it is possible to cut slab stock and get good cushions. At the same time, molding can be done with these polyether foam-prepolymers. When the polyethers are used, it is necessary to employ the prepolymer technique; the one-shot method is not adaptable. This requires an extra step in processing with more difficult storaging problems, etc. However, it is highly possible that these new flexible foams based on polyether polyurethanes will capture a large part of the cushioning market.

6. RUBBERS

One of the more promising fields for the application of polyurethanes is that represented by the solid elastomers, commonly called "urethane rubber." The polyurethanes have demonstrated unusually high abrasion resistance, high tear strength, and excellent shock absorption, coupled with hardness, a wide range of flexibility and elasticity, solvent resistance (especially to hydrocarbons), and excellent resistance to oxygen aging. They have certain disadvantages, but these are being corrected by further research. For example, they exhibit a tendency toward poor resistance to high temperatures, hot water, steam, and other hydrolytic agents. A new development, "Adiprene C," has made good progress in overcoming the hydrolytic unstability. Rubbers made from polyesters have higher brittle points than natural rubber. While cured natural rubber gum can be used to −65°C, one type of urethane rubber, cured "Chemigum S L," is good only to −35°C. DuPont claims that "Adiprene B" will not freeze even on prolonged exposure at −40°C, and that "Adiprene C" will not become brittle until temperatures below −95°F are reached. However, the physical properties of these new rubbers are so outstanding that much research has been done, and is being done, to improve them and to find new applications for them. Some of the present applications are chute linings, such as used for the transportation of abrasive materials; industrial, passenger and truck tires; shock absorption gears, etc. Many of the future applications may be based on the ease with which these materials can be cast. Hence, it will be possible to produce fairly complex forms which may be used for machinery parts.

It may be noted that similarities of applications and properties of the various polyurethane rubbers may be found. Since most of the urethane rubbers are abrasion resistant, it will be possible to use practically all of them in applications which depend on this property.

There are four distinct lines of experimentation for the urethane rubbers; each, in general, deals with one type, and has a single research group, either national or corporative, involved.

"Vulcollan"

"Vulcollan" is the original urethane rubber developed in Germany. This group of polyurethanes is based on the reaction products of various diisocyanates and polyesters. The principles developed in its research demonstrate those involved in the general field of urethane rubbers. In 1940, the initial work was started on these products when Schlack reacted polyesters with diisocyanates, with some promise of elasticity in the products. Pinten produced highly elastic products by the incorporation of some trifunctional alcohols in the polyesters. However, the resulting elastomers had poor tear strengths. It is interesting to observe that the introduction of branching by the use of triisocyanates produced similar effects. Apparently, the proper type of branching must be that which is created by the further reaction of excess diisocyanate with the hydrogen in the urea, amide and urethane linkages which forms the corresponding biurets, acyl amides and allophanates.

A typical preparation for a "Vulcollan" will be given with comments to illustrate the experimentation involved in its production. The first step consists of preparing a linear polyester in the molecular weight range of 2000 to 2500. Fourteen moles of ethylene glycol is esterified with 13 moles of adipic acid; the reaction is completed by subsequent heating under vacuum. The resulting polyester is a hard wax, with a softening range of 60 to 70°C. As a generalization, polyesters having hydroxyl numbers between 20 and 60, and acid values of about 1, have been found to be particularly good for the preparation of urethane rubbers. Various dibasic acids and glycols were studied. Table 6.1 gives some of the results obtained, especially as they relate to "Vulcollan."

The data, especially that given in the last column, may be used as a crude sieving device to delineate profitable avenues of endeavor. Thus, it may be noted that, of the dibasic acids, those with short-chain lengths (succinic acid) and with aromatic structure (phthalic acid) are not suitable. Adipic acid shows the best promise, which is quite fortunate since it is a reasonably priced dibasic acid and readily available. Considering the glycol component, it is found that, although ethylene glycol produces "Vulcollans" of excellent physical properties, their brittle points are too high and they have a tendency to harden. On the other hand, propylene glycol-1,2 and butylene glycol-2,3 produce "Vulcollans" with lower brittle points, but with reduced physical properties. A compromise between these two states is definitely desirable.

Further studies revealed the feasibility of blending polyethylene adipate with polypropylene adipate to obtain properties in between. A solution consisting of 70 per cent ethylene and 30 per cent propylene glycol esters was suggested. This was found to prevent any hardening of the final product.

TABLE 6.1. REACTION PRODUCTS OF POLYESTERS WITH NAPHTHYLENE-1,5-DIISOCYANATE

Glycol	Dibasic Acid	Polyester Consistency	Tensile Strength (psi)	Elongation (%)	Tear Strength (psi)	Remarks
Ethylene	Succinic	Solid wax	3900	625	1700	High permanent set; hardens and becomes leathery
Ethylene	Adipic	Solid wax	5000	640	2200	Hardens slowly
Ethylene	Sebacic	Solid wax	—	—	—	Hardens immediately on cooling; only highly elastic at elevated temperatures
Ethylene	Diglycolic	Resin	3900	570	2100	Leathery; very easily saponified
Ethylene	Phthalic	Brittle resin	(1500)	(260)	(1200)	Processible only with 25% di-butyl phthalate; glass hard without plasticizer
1,2-Propylene	Succinic	Liquid	2500	670	1400	Leathery; highly elastic at 70°C
1,2-Propylene	Adipic	Liquid	3100	780	1300	Does not harden
2,3-Butylene	Adipic	Liquid	2500	630	1300	Does not harden
1,6-Hexanediol	Adipic	Solid wax	3500	610	1700	Leathery

In the experiments reported in Table 6.1, only naph-thylene-1,5-diisocyanate was used to make the isocyanate polyester. Other diisocyanates were studied, and Table 6.2 gives a sample of the results obtained. The experimentation from which the data were taken for this table was apparently done early in the research program. This conclusion may be drawn from the fact that the basic polyester used was an undried polyethylene adipate. Later work showed the need for an anhydrous ester in order to obtain a good prod-uct. In each case the "Vulcollans" were produced with a 30 per cent molar excess of the diisocyanate which is being used.

TABLE 6.2. DIISOCYANATE STUDY

Diisocyanate	Tensile Strength (psi)	Elongation (%)	Tear Strength (psi)
1. Hexamethylene	—	—	—
2. Tolylene-2,4	(2800-3500)	(730)	(1200)
3. 2-Nitrodiphenyl-4,4′	2700	743	1700
4. Diphenyl sulfone-4,4′	3100	331	2000
5. Naphthylene-1,4	4500	756	1900
6. Naphthylene-1,5	4500	765	2400
7. Naphthylene-2,7	5700	758	2300
8. Fluorene	6200	660	2000

The "Vulcollan" made from hexamethylene diisocyanate was worthless; it hardened immediately, whereas that made from tolylene diisocyanate had a high permanent set, showed bad blistering, and was not reproducible. The gen-eral conclusion of the investigators was that a certain rigid expanse in the structure of the diisocyanate was necessary, and that naphthylene-1,5-diisocyanate was exceptionally adaptable to this product.

The final operation, which may be considered to be a cure, involved cross-linking the isocyanate polyester by the use of water. Several methods were used, one of which was to pass steam through the dough until the proper consistency was obtained. The preferred method employed a kneading machine in which a controlled amount of water was added to produce a sheet which could be used for further molding. These molded products have been used for slabs, shoe soles and heels, as well as packing, etc. Chemicals other than water have been found to be good cross-linking agents. Table 6-3 illustrates some diols that were used. The isocyanate polyester used was made from polypropylene adipate and naphthylene-1,5-diisocyanate.

TABLE 6.3. CROSS-LINKING AGENTS

Cross-Linking Agent	%	Tensile Strength (psi)	Elongation at Break	Tear Strength (psi)
Butynediol	2.0	4550	640	2260
Triethylene glycol	2.0	2250	925	534
Dimethyl propylene glycol	2.2	3130	780	590
Glycerol monophenyl ether	2.0	2630	900	534
Thiodiethylene glycol	2.2	2490	715	1070

Butynediol compares quite favorably with water curing; the others do not. The rather rigid acetylenic bond demonstrates good cross-linking. Liquid casting processes are made possible by the ability to use cross-linking agents other than water.

As mentioned previously, the "Vulcollans" show extremely good resistance to initiation and propagation of tearing. They also show excellent resistance to abrasion and, hence,

---

* An excellent detailed study of the above experimentation may be found in *Rubber Chemistry and Technology*, **23**, 812-35 (1950).

are used in products which may be subjected to severe wear, such as heels of shoes. Another outstanding property is their low permeability to gases of the order of $1/10$ to $1/20$ that of natural rubber. The "Vulcollans" are resistant to hydrocarbon solvents, but not to hydrolytic solvents. Boiling water will decompose them. Their resistance to dry heat is relatively poor; however, as an offset to this, their resistance to oxidation is good. Many of the applications developed in Germany have been based on these advantages and disadvantages.

Mobay and their licensees have carried on the work on "Vulcollans" in the United States. Their formulations are based on a polyester called Multron R-14 and an isocyanate component Mondur N-5. At present, they are preparing rubber by casting, in which case the prepolymer is cured by a cross-linking agent. Development of a second method adaptable to processing on rubber equipment is being pursued, in which a stable, raw gum may be cured by adding more polyisocyanate or by some other means. Several licensees of Mobay are selling articles made of "Vulkollan" (Mobay's trade name for urethane rubber). Figure 6.1 shows some of these. Many of the applications follow the German practice. Thus, we find heels, gears, shock absorbers, check valves, solid tires, etc. for industrial use.

A more recent "Vulkollan," namely, "Vulkollan 30," has been developed, which combines hardness (Shore A95) with high elasticity and appropriate hysteresis to give excellent shock absorbing power and vibration dampening. Hence, it has been used for shock absorption pads of various types. It can be used as a head for a mallet to drive a tenpenny nail into oak, but it will not mar a polished mahogany desk top. Used as handles on air hammers, it will absorb shock, and at the same time remain hard enough to permit the application of adequate pressure. These few examples illustrate the vast potential for urethane rubbers.

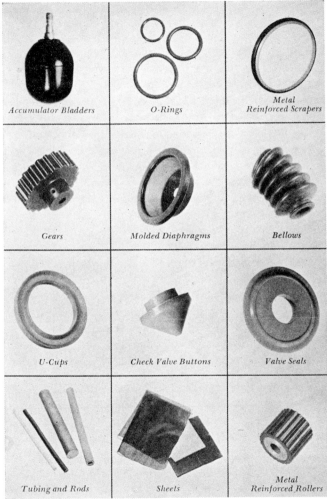

Accumulator Bladders *O-Rings* *Metal Reinforced Scrapers*

Gears *Molded Diaphragms* *Bellows*

U-Cups *Check Valve Buttons* *Valve Seals*

Tubing and Rods *Sheets* *Metal Reinforced Rollers*

(*Courtesy Greer Industries, Inc.*)

Figure 6.1. The above illustration shows a few manufactured products using "Disogrin," a diisocyanate polyester elastomer, belonging to the same chemical family as "Vulkollan."

"Chemigum SL"

One disadvantage of "Vulcollan" products is the comparatively short shelf life of the isocyanate-polyester condensations. This makes it necessary to start the cure of urethane rubber soon after the condensation takes place. "Chemigum SL" was developed by the Goodyear Tire & Rubber Company to overcome this handicap. Their approach was to use a deficit of diisocyanate rather than an excess (as in the German processes) and to employ more diisocyanate (not necessarily the same one) to cure the condensate. The uncured stock can be processed or stored. Physically, it has many of the characteristics of pale crepe rubber. By employing curing agents, these condensates can be handled with the usual rubber equipment, including mills and molds. The cured urethane rubbers are quite similar to the "Vulcollans" in both physical and chemical properties. They exhibit unusual toughness, excellent tear resistance; in fact, they have all the expected advantages over natural rubber and GR-S. Thus, it may be said that "Chemigum SL" represents a different route to a "Vulcollan."

The preparation of "Chemigum SL" is quite similar to that described above for "Vulcollan." The linear polyester is heated at 120°C with a diisocyanate, using a molar quantity of the diisocyanate in the range of 70 to 99 per cent of theory. The condensation products have molecular weights between 25,000 to 50,000 and are claimed to have comparatively long storage life (no crystallization in 6 to 12 months). Additional isocyanate is used to introduce the cross-linking necessary for the cure. This may be done on a mill. The cured products have the same disadvantages found in cured "Vulcollan." Thus, it is found that the freezing point is only −35°C, compared to −65°C for cured natural rubber gum. [Polyester urethane rubber made from caprolactones (see Chapter 5) has much lower freezing points]. The poor resistance to high temperatures, both wet and dry, is the biggest disadvantage of both "Vulcollan" and "Chemigum SL," as can be seen in Table 6.4.

TABLE 6.4. AGING PROPERTIES OF VULCANIZED "CHEMIGUM SL"

Treatment		Tensile Strength (psi)	Elongation (%)
Original		5450	750
Dry Heat Aging			
Temperature °F	Time Days		
158	30	4700	685
250	14	500	580
Aging in Water			
Temperature °F	Time Days		
77	90	5000	
158	14	1700	
200	2	1000	

On the other hand their resistance to oxidation and ultraviolet is excellent and they have low oxygen absorption, as compared to the hydrocarbon rubbers. Thus, at 100°C, tread stock natural rubber will absorb 92 ml of oxygen per gram; GR-S, being somewhat better, will absorb only 18 ml; "Chemigum SL" is far better and absorbs only 0.08 ml. Hence, we find the same advantages and disadvantages for both of the urethane rubbers based on polyesters. It is reasonable to expect that some of their uses may overlap.

This urethane rubber has been successfully used as solid tires for industrial equipment. It is adhered with isocyanate cement and gives far better service life than rubber, with a minimum of chipping or cutting. In addition, these tires permit doubling the load. An excellent application is for valve inserts in high-pressure mud pumps used in oil drilling operations, where they give four times the service life of other materials. Another good application is for the inner walls of hose and chutes used to transport sand and other abrasive materials. Again, as with "Vulkollan," uses which require shock absorption are feasible. The use of the raw gum in a solvent for coating various plastics and yarns to produce a flexible, scuff-resistant and weather-resistant finish has been suggested.

"Vulcaprene A"

This urethane rubber is closely related to "Vulcollan" and "Chemigum SL." Though it is mainly an English development (The Imperial Chemical Industries has done intensive experimentation along these lines), the basic patents in the United States and Great Britain are held by duPont. In place of polyesters, polyesteramides are used to condense with diisocyanates. Thus, a portion of the glycols normally used in formation of the polyesters is replaced by amino glycols, diamines, etc. The preferred method is the substitution of some glycol by ethanolamine. The tear strength of the rubbers is relatively poor. In actual production, "Chemigum SL," which has a deficit of diisocyanates, is used as the model for gum stock rather than "Vulcollan" which has an excess of diisocyanate. In curing, formaldehyde may be used to cross-link the amide linkages or more diisocyanate may be added, as in the case of "Chemigum SL." The main application for "Vulcaprene A" is in coatings, where it appears to function as a novel vulcanizable polymeric plasticizer for other plastics.

"Vulcaprene," physically mixed with various plastics and degraded proteins in a wide range of percentage, is used as a coating material. These mixtures may be cured by either of the agents previously mentioned. They have the advantage of excellent abrasion and flex resistance. The presence of the companion plastic tends to increase the resistance of "Vulcaprene A" to hydrolytic agents. Blends with polyvinyl formal are typical of such mixtures.

TABLE 6.5. HARDNESS OF VULCAPRENE/POLYVINYL MIXTURES (CURED)

Polyvinyl formal (%)	50	30	20	10
Vulcaprene (%)	50	70	80	90
Shore hardness	96	82	63	48

The two ingredients are miscible in all proportions and are easily blended by working finely divided polyvinyl formal into uncured "Vulcaprene" on a rubber mill at 120°C. The products are homogeneous, leathery sheets which vary from a soft, rubbery material, when the "Vulcaprene" content is high, to a hard, brittle material.

Curing is required to produce thermosetting products. The preferred blend is one in which 70 per cent "Vulcaprene" to 30 per cent formal is used. The blends are made into doughs with chlorinated solvents, and spread on cloth in the conventional manner. Uncured, tough, flexible, but thermoplastic coatings are obtained. Upon curing, these coatings develop resistance to abrasion and flex and lose their thermoplasticity. Superior leather cloths are reported to have been made in this manner. Other plastics which have promise for "Vulcaprene" blends are nitrocellulose, cellulose acetate, hydrolyzed leather, etc.

"Adiprene"

"Adiprene B," a duPont development, was based on polyether glycol, rather than polyesters. When cured, it produced a urethane rubber of usual high strength and abrasion resistance; it also had the solvent and ozone resistances expected of these urethane rubbers. In addition, it showed no tendency to freeze even after prolonged exposure at −40°C—an improvement over the polyester urethane rubbers. The uncured raw gum was a transparent, amber-colored polymer with a molecular weight of about 30,000. It was necessary to react it with more diisocyanate in order to cure it. This, together with the excellent stability of the raw gum, shows that the chemical properties of "Adiprene B" is closer to "Chemigum SL" than "Vulcollan." However, it also had the hydrolytic aging disadvantage characteristic of the other urethane rubbers.

TABLE 6.6. AGING PROPERTIES OF CURED "ADIPRENE B"

Aging Conditions	Tensile Strength (psi)
Control	5600
Water at 25°C, 14 days	6000
Water at 70°C, 7 days	4200
Water at 100°C, 1 day	1900
Oxygen bomb, 21 days at 70°C	4800
Dry Air at 121°C, 14 days	3200

Table 6.6 shows that the resistance of "Adiprene B" to oxidation is excellent, but its reaction with hydrolytic agents is similar to "Chemigum SL" and "Vulcollan."

An interesting observation made during the study of "Adiprene B" was that, in contradiction to the polyester-based polyurethanes, it could be reinforced with carbon blacks and silicas to improve its hot tensile strength, abrasion resistance, and tear strength. This effect is found to be even more significant in an improved Adiprene—namely, "Adiprene C." In addition to being moisture-sensitive, "Adiprene B" had the disadvantage of being extremely difficult to process. To overcome these shortcomings, "Adiprene C" was developed, and introduced as an excellent all-purpose type polymer. When cured, it has good abrasion resistance and an order of solvent resistance equivalent to the buna-N type polymers. The differences between this and the previous urethane rubbers are:

(1) Excellent low temperature properties; does not become brittle until temperatures below −95°F are reached.

TABLE 6.7. EFFECT OF CARBON BLACK CONCENTRATION

Adiprene C		100				
HAF Carbon Black		As shown				
MBTS		3				
MBT		1				
Sulfur		1.5				
Activator, RCD-2098		0.35				
Cure: 90′/284°F						
HAF Parts	0	10	20	30	40	50
Stress-Strain at 25°C						
Modulus at 300% (psi)	360	1020	1900	3550	4200	5100
Tensile strength at break (psi)	1400	2850	3600	5100	5100	5100
Elongation at break (%)	480	440	430	370	340	300
Hardness, Shore A	57	60	67	72	76	80
ASTM Resilience (%)	82	80	78	74	70	65
Compression Set, Method B (%)	20	20	20	20	20	19
Conditioned 22 hr @ 70°C						

TABLE 6.8. AGING RESISTANCE OF "ADIPRENE C" VULCANIZATES

Adiprene C	100
HAF Carbon Black	30
Cumar W 2½	10
Sulfur	1.5
MBTS	3
MBT	1
Activator, RCD-2098	0.35

Cure: 60′/280°F

	Modulus at 300% (psi)	Tensile at Break (psi)	Elongation at Break (%)	Hardness Shore A
Original	2000	4700	540	70
Heat aging*				
14 days at 70°C	2625	4100	460	75
14 days at 100°C	—	3025	280	75
14 days at 121°C	—	2525	240	74
Water resistance**				
14 days at 25°C	1950	3900	510	68
14 days at 70°C	1775	3575	510	67
3 days at 100°C	2200	3400	420	68
Oxygen bomb**				
21 days at 70°C, 300 psi	2500	4175	500	70

Ozone exposure—bent loop

    1 ppm Concentration
      170 hours to trace cracking, no change to 270 hours
    100 ppm Concentration
      4 hours to trace cracking, 8 hours to slight, 170 hours to noticeable, no change to 270 hours

The resistance of "Adiprene C" to swell or degradation in commercial automative or aviation fluids is excellent. Although other oil resistant elastomers may show some advantage in certain oils, "Adiprene C" represents the best in overall oil resistance.

* Tentative Method ASTM D 865-52.
** ASTM D 471-52T.
*** ASTM D 572-52.

(2) Carbon black increases its physical properties markedly.

(3) Can be cured with sulphur. Storage life of raw gum up to 100°F is excellent. A year's storage showed essentially no effect.

(4) Can be used for parts employed in the temperature range of 250°F.

(5) Has good resistance to hydrolytic agents.

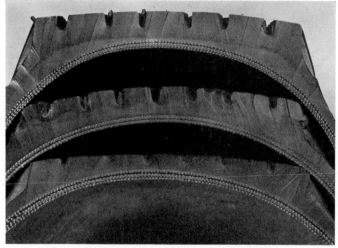

(*Courtesy E. I. du Pont de Nemours & Co., Inc.*)

Figure 6.2. Top: Original "Adiprene C" tread. Middle: "Adiprene C" tread after 28,000 miles. Bottom: GRS tread after 28,000 miles.

"Adiprene C" is expected to find its biggest application in tread stocks for passenger cars and truck tires. Urethane rubber does not form a cured bond with natural rubber or GR-S; hence, cements are required. Figure 6.2 shows a

sequence of tire treads which demonstrates the superiority
of this material over GR-S. Figure 6.3 illustrates the handling and testing methods used. Another promising use is in
shoe heels. Because of its resistance to oil, it has been proposed that "Adiprene C" be used in oil well parts. (Figure 6.4)

(Courtesy E. I. du Pont de Nemours & Co., Inc.)

Figure 6.3.   "Adiprene C" tread being tested on a tire wheel.

"Adiprene L" is presently in the development stage at
duPont. It may be cured by polyols, titanate esters, and
amines. The properties of cured "Adiprene L" are similar
to Adiprene C, and the processing equipment available
determines which one will be used. "Adiprene L" is quite

(Courtesy E. I. du Pont de Nemours & Co., Inc.)

Figure 6.4. The three molded pieces in the center are oil well parts; the heels are made of "Adiprene C"; the other parts are made of "Adiprene L".

low in viscosity and, hence, may be molded in intricate shapes if degassing operations are included. It is being evaluated in coating, caulking and casting applications.

7. ADHESIVES

The application of diisocyanates in the field of adhesives is a sphere of activity in which both American and German investigators have worked for many years. In the case of the Germans, we have an idea of the historical developments that led to the discovery of the advantages found in using the diisocyanates. The Rubber Laboratory of I. G. Farbenindustrie A.G. had the problem of vulcanizing Buna by the addition of diisocyanates to Buna copolymers containing hydroxyl groups. It was soon noted that Buna S, which is apparently free of hydroxyl groups, reacted with the diisocyanates. However, more important was the observation that these vulcanized materials adhered strongly to the metal parts of the vulcanizing press. To the Germans, this was the clue to the long-sought bonding agent to be used with the Bunas. It was found that Buna-sulfur mixtures could be attached to iron, light metals, porcelain, etc., with heat-resistant bonds. Adhesive strengths up to 1,200 psi were obtained, rupture occurring in the rubber and not at the bond. Accordingly, *meta*-tolylene diisocyanate and hexamethylene diisocyanate (sold under the trade names "Vulkollan T" and "H," respectively) were employed in the war effort for bonding Buna rubbers to metals for tank caterpillar treads, etc. The success of the diisocyanates during the war led to their investigation in the broad field of adhesives.

Most of the subsequent German developments were two-fold. First, they used combinations of the Desmophens and Desmodurs to produce bonds consisting of polyurethanes; secondly, they employed the triisocyanate-Desmodur R, mainly as an adhesive additive. The combinations were sold under the name of "Polystal." One combination, used for adhering wood-to-wood and wood-to-iron, in order to produce tough bonds which could be cured at room temperature and which would withstand vibration consisted of the following:

40 parts—Polystal U-I —a 70% solution of Desmophen 900 in ethyl acetate

100 parts—Polyestal U-II—a 75% solution of Desmodur HH in ethyl acetate

Once the two solutions are blended, the mixture has a pot life of 8 to 10 hours; of course, traces of alkali, acid, heat and amines will decrease this period. Hence, temperature and accelerators are used to control the setting time of the adhesive.

TABLE 7.1. SETTING TIME

Temperature	Accelerator (Trimethylamine)	Time
Room	none	1-2 days
Room	present	3 hours
10°C	present	4-5 hours
0°C	present	7 hours
less than 0°C	present	overnight

This showed much superiority over the then conventional urea formaldehyde adhesives, that it was given priority in the airplane industry. It can be cured at a much lower temperature (see Table 7.1). In addition, its bonds showed better resistance to hot water and heat, as well as excellent mechanical properties and elasticity.

The use of the Desmophens and Desmodurs permits the fabricator to vary the flexibility of the resultant bond. A combination suggested which will yield a fairly rigid bond for adhering iron-to-iron, porcelain-to-porcelain or iron, light metals to each other or iron, and phenol formaldehyde plastics to each other, is:

> 200 parts—Desmophen 800 (75% solution in ethyl
> acetate)
>
> 100 parts—Desmodur T (no solvent)

A working span of 6 hours at room temperature is possible with this adhesive. A more flexible bond is obtained with the following formulation:

> 300 parts—Desmophen 1200 (80% solution in
> ethyl acetate)
>
> 100 parts—Desmodur T (no solvent)

The adhesive is applied by spreading it on one of the roughened surfaces of the materials being bonded. After allowing the solvent to evaporate (10 to 15 minutes), the pieces are clamped together with adequate pressure to hold them firmly, but not enough to squeeze out the adhesive (0.67 oz per sq ft is suggested). Curing requires 24 hours at room temperature, 2 to 3 hours at 90 to 100°C, or one-half hour at 150°C. Solvent and water-resistant bonds are obtained. Furthermore, in tearing tests, the breakdown occurs in breakage of the material. For example, in the case of glass as one substrate, glass splinters are torn out. These three adhesive combinations are typical of the German technique using polyurethanes.

Desmodur R was found to give excellent bonding effects, either by itself, in rubber cements, or in combinations with polyesters. This triisocyanate has a melting point of 90°C when pure; technically, it is obtained as a reddish honey-like syrup; it is used as a 20 per cent solution in methylene chloride. Its largest use was in the adhesion of various materials to Buna. Thus, in manufacturing tires, it has been found that, since synthetic fibers have smooth surfaces, it is difficult to make them adhere to rubber. However, the use of this particular triisocyanate produces good bonds.

TABLE 7.2. RUBBER-TO-FABRIC ADHESION

Fabric	Load to Peel (Pound Per Inch)	
	0% Isocyanate	20% Isocyanate
Cotton	20	20
Nylon	2½	8
Rayon	7	19

The natural rough surface of cotton needs no aid for adhesion, but the synthetic fibers do. In rubber cements the use of 5 to 10 parts by weight of Desmodur R per 100 parts of rubber cement has been recommended; otherwise dilute solutions of the cement in methylene chloride should be used. To cement vulcanized Buna to steel, combinations with polyesters are suggested. In breaking tests, it is the materials that break, rather than the bonds. One of the drawbacks in the use of triphenylmethane triisocyanate is its high price. Recently, a new liquid polyisocyanate, polyaryl polyisocyanate (PAPI), has been introduced on the American market. This material is similar to a triisocyanate; it is felt that this more reasonably priced chemical may be used advantageously in the adhesive field.

In the early 1940's, the American patent literature revealed an interest in the use of diisocyanates to bond rubber to various materials, particularly fibers. Here, the art consisted of using the diisocyanates as adhesive additives in rubber cements. Thus, the use of 10 parts of hexamethylene diisocyanate to 100 parts of a 10 per cent solution of 90 plasticity pale crepe rubber in toluene was suggested. These products tended to gel and had comparatively poor shelf-lives. An exception was methylene bis(p-phenylene isocyanate), which had good shelf-life. A cement of this type was made, and in a period of 20 weeks it showed no increase in viscosity; in addition, when used at various times during this period, it produced as good a bond as it had originally. The results were superior to the then conventional resorcinol-formaldehyde latex cements.

TABLE 7.3. BONDING VISCOSE RAYON TO AN ELASTOMER
COMPOSITION: EFFECT OF STORAGE ON CEMENT

Vulcanizable Elastomer Carcass Stock	% Cement on Fabric	Pull (Lbs Per Linear Inch—25°C)				
		1 day	4 wks	12 wks	16 wks	20 wks
Rubber	0	3.0	—	—	—	—
	5	20	26	21	20	21
	10	30	31	35	31	32
Buna S	0	3.0	—	—	—	—
	5	20	21	22	20	21
	10	30	32	33	32	33

Solutions of this diisocyanate in o-dichlorobenzene have been found to produce excellent adhesion between various elastomers and metals. The bonds have excellent resistance to elevated temperatures, flexing and impact, and are not affected by oils and solvents. Relative humidity has an effect upon the final bond. This may be minimized by incorporating the isocyanate in rubber cements. Table 7.4 shows the results which can be obtained by using a 50 per cent solution of diphenyl-methane-4,4-diisocyanate (MDI).

TABLE 7.4. ADHESION OF NEOPRENE TYPE W COMPOUND
TO VARIOUS METALS

Metal Surfaces	Adhesion (psi)
Steel	1100
Brass	1050
Stainless steel	1200
Aluminum	1325
Copper	950

The metal surfaces were sandblasted and, after application of one thin coat of MDI solution, were conditioned for 19 hours at 50 per cent relative humidity, assembled using a Neoprene Type W stock, and vulcanized immediately. Satisfactory adhesion was obtained to all the metals used. Similar results have been reported for other elastomers, such as rubber, Buna N, etc.

Combinations of polyesters and diisocyanates (and their derivatives) require prompt use of the adhesive since their pot lives are short. Prior to its agreement with Bayer, Monsanto studied a somewhat different type of adhesive, namely, adducts of isocyanates and polyols, in which twice the equivalent ratio of isocyanate is used. These products had enhanced storage life, if they were properly stored and kept free of moisture. This study is of two-fold interest. First, there was the storage life study; and, secondly, three possible methods were investigated which used these adducts for adhesion. A typical adduct is that made from one mole of polyethylene glycol 400 (molecular weight—400) and two moles of toluene diisocyanate. The glycol is added to the isocyanate slowly, with agitation. After an induction period of 5 to 10 minutes, an exothermic reaction takes place, causing a rise in temperature to 80 to 120°C. After the reaction subsides, the reaction mass is heated at 80 to 100°C for 30 minutes to complete the reactions. A viscous amber liquid resulted. This is the principal procedure employed. Products were obtained, depending upon the polyol and diisocyanate, which varied in consistency from glasses to viscous liquids. Dry benzene may also be used as a solvent during the reaction, or after. If the adduct is kept free of moisture, it can only react further by combining with urethane linkage to introduce cross-linking. Table 7.5 illustrates the effect of temperature, catalyst and time. The apparent stability of the adduct, even in the presence of N-methyl morpholine, is striking. This factor alone should cause interest in the use of these products.

TABLE 7.5. STORAGE AGING OF P400—TOLYLENE DIISOCYANATE ADDUCT (TDI)

Temp.	Conditions Time	Solvent	Catalyst	Results
R.T.	12 months	none	none	no apparent change
50°C	12 months	50% Benzene	none	stable
5°C	12 months	50% Benzene	none	stable
5°C	12 months	50% Benzene	2½% N-methyl morpholine	stable
R.T.	3 months	50% Benzene	same	jelled to solid
50°C	1 month	50% Benzene	same	jelled to solid

In using these adducts as adhesives, the curing (or polymerization) of the adduct is carried out in two stages. First, the molecular chain is lengthened by the water reaction, and this is followed by cross-linking through the urethane or urea linkage with time and temperature. Three methods of cross-linking were suggested.

(1) *Low-Temperature Bonding.* A 50 per cent solution

of catalyzed adduct in benzene is applied in thin film on each of the surfaces. Evaporation of the solvent and reaction with moisture from the air are allowed to take place. When the adhesion layers have been cured to a very tacky state (roughly 10 minutes), they are brought together with enough pressure for good contact. The final cure may proceed at or slightly above room temperature; because of this, adhesion of heat-sensitive materials is promising with these adducts.

Much work is still needed in order to utilize this method. Variations in humidity, room temperature and reproducibility in adduct formation have interfered with the determination of the desired extent of open cure. Performing the closed cure at 100°C has ironed out some of the uncertainties mentioned, as shown in Table 7.6.

TABLE 7.6. TENSILE STRENGTH OF ADDUCT ADHESIVES

Materials Bonded*	Adduct		Average Tensile Strength of Bond (psi)
	Diisocyanate	Glycol	
Steel to glass	Toluene-2,4	Polyethylene 400	900
Steel to cellulose acetate	Diphenyl methane	Monoglyceride of hard fatty acids	600
Aluminum to polymethyl methacrylate	Diphenyl methane	Polypropylene glycol 750	350
Aluminum to cellulose acetate	Toluene-2,4	Polypropylene glycol	450

* Assemblies given open cure of 10 minutes at room temperature and 50 to 70 per cent relative humidity, and a closed cure of 30 minutes at 100°C.

(2) *High-Temperature Bonding.* Where materials to be bonded are not heat-sensitive, more latitude is enjoyed. Thin coatings of adducts are used. The open cure is done with

dry steam. The time depends on the temperature and catalyst. The closed cure is usually performed at 150 to 300°C,
high enough to melt the adhesive layer. After cooling, the
full strength of the bond is obtained. An extra advantage
of this method is that much time (up to a month) can
elapse between the two cures. An example is the bonding
of steel with a 50 per cent benzene solution of toluene
diisocyanate-polyethylene 400 adduct, containing a 2.5 per
cent catalyst. The open cure was done at room temperature,
and the closed cure was 1 minute at 225°C and 150 psi
pressure. A bond tensile strength of 1,500 psi was obtained.

(3) *Thermoplastic Bonding with Dry Adhesive.* Method
(2) has been modified in such a manner that bonding takes
place without coating the surface being bonded. A carrier
(see Table 7.7) is coated with the adhesive and completely
cured. These coated, cured carriers are placed cut-to-size
between the surfaces being bonded. Heat and pressure are
applied to melt the adhesive layer.

TABLE 7.7.   COATED CARRIER CHARACTERISTICS:
EFFECT ON BOND STRENGTH

Carrier	Thickness (in.)	Adhesive Film* Thickness (in.)	Bond Tensile** Strength (psi)
Aluminum foil	0.001	0.0035	1640
Copper foil	0.002	0.0031	626
Lead foil	0.0035	0.0030	936
Tissue paper	0.0015	0.0021	722

* Coated thickness less original thickness divided by 2.
** When used to bond steel to steel.

The adhesive of method (2) was used in the examples
given in Table 7.7. The carrier was cured with steam
at 100°C for 2 minutes. Final bonding was performed by
heating the resulting foils between pieces of steel for 1

minute at 225°C, under 150 psi. Table 7.8 gives the results of this technique with other metals. Only aluminum foil was used, with a bond cure of 175°C, at 50 psi pressure, for 10 minutes.

TABLE 7.8. METAL-TO-METAL BONDING

Metals	Bond Tensile Strength (psi)
Steel (called rolled)	1600
Aluminum (24 ST)	over 2,000
Magnesium (Dow metal FS-1)	800

These techniques show promise. The possibilities for variations are quite large, both from the standpoint of materials and handling. However, it must be recognized that much work still needs to be done.

More recently, experimental work along these lines was done using a castor oil (1 mole) and "Nacconate 300" (MDI) (3 moles) adduct. The bonding may be done at room temperature and with contact pressure. Bond strengths of 1,500 psi are claimed for aluminum bonded to itself. The concentrated prepolymer has a shelf-life of over 3 months. The suggested method of bonding is somewhat different than above. The prepolymer is dissolved to 50 per cent solids in a 50 per cent solution of acetone in toluene containing 0.5 to 1.0 per cent N-methyl morpholine. Both surfaces are brushed with this solution; an open cure time of about 10 to 15 minutes is allowed before a bond is made. In 3 hours, the bond can undergo light service; but, in 24 hours, full strength is obtained. This formulation is recommended for bonding wood, glass, leather, vinyl sheeting, etc., to themselves or to other materials.

8. COATINGS

One of the more fertile commercial fields for polyure-thanes is that of coating applications. Early in the develop-ment of diisocyanate products, it was recognized that they could be used as lacquers; in fact, it was thought that they might extend the areas in which lacquers were used. Thus, coatings upon such substrates as paper, textiles, leather, etc., were made possible. The resulting films exhibited extra-ordinary adhesiveness, high gloss, water and solvent re-sistance, excellent electrical properties, low gas permeability and all-around good weather resistance. They could be pre-pared in various degrees of flexibility and under wide tem-perature conditions. It is possible to apply and cure them on such fragile surfaces as paper, or to bake them on wire at somewhat elevated temperatures. Consequently, it is not surprising that the art of these coatings has been developed to a high degree in Germany. During World War II, paper was impregnated with polyurethanes for the production of mustard-gas resistant garments. They were used to produce high gloss finishes on airplanes to eke out extra speed. At present, industrial finishes are important because it is pos-sible to take advantage of the inherent flexibility in their formulation to obtain more desirable characteristics. It is reported that polyurethanes are being used in chemical plants to produce excellent anti-corrosion coatings. Some of these will be briefly mentioned. The coating of a reaction kettle, which had an overflow problem of gasoline and acetic acid, and had to be reapplied every year was replaced by a urethane coating. It was in excellent condition after 14 months. A urethane coating on a water-gas generator showed no failure or metal corrosion after 6 years, except for some loss in gloss, although it was subjected to gases and physical strain as a result of changing temperatures varying between freezing and 250°F. In general, these coatings have been used in steel forging shops, slaughter houses, dairies and breweries, as well as chemical plants. They have to withstand heat and chemical vapors and spillage, as well as continuous moisture and cleaning processes. In addition, they have exhibited high impact and abrasion resistance, as well as excellent adhesion to various building materials. Many other applications of German technique may be found in the booklet, "Surface Coatings," by the Mobay Chemical Company. In the United States, considerable interest has been shown in these products. Wire coatings and abrasive-resistant finishes appear to be the most active fields.

As mentioned previously, any polyhydroxyl material may be reacted with a diisocyanate-bearing product to produce polyurethanes. This holds true most strongly in the coating field. The variety of these two components is tremendous. However, the traditional German methods are based on combinations of the Desmodur-Desmophen types. Initially, the Desmophens were dried and dissolved in non-alcoholic solvents, such as ethyl acetate and toluene, and then reacted with tolylene diisocyanate dissolved in similar solutions. These two-component systems had pot lives of the order of one day. They could be sprayed on surfaces and allowed to air dry at ambient temperatures, or they could be applied and baked at temperatures up to 150°C. Excellent properties were obtained with these coatings. Their flexibility range was wide; the softer or more elastic films were made with the higher numbered Desmophens, and the harder films with the lower numbered ones, which have the most cross-linking.

Blends of these resins produced a spectrum of hardness and elasticity. These products had several operational disadvantages: (1) the pot life was considered too short, (2) there was a need for alcohol-free solvents, and (3) and most important, was the irritant effects of the diisocyanates. The latter was found particularly bad in spraying lacquers. In fact, most of the more serious cases of isocyanate irritation in Europe resulted from this operation. This shortcoming could be overcome by proper ventilation.

Very early in the development of isocyanate products it was found that isocyanate irritation was caused by the comparatively high vapor pressures of the offending diisocyanate. Hence, as a step toward eliminating the irritating effects of tolylene diisocyanate, attempts were made to decrease its vapor pressure by reacting it partially. Commercially, this is done by reacting one mole of a triol such as hexanetriol-1,2,6 with 3 moles of the diisocyanate. The hexanetriol is added, drop-wise, to a solution of the tolylene diisocyanate in dry ethyl acetate, and cooled. The final product is a resin (with solvent removed). Other triols may be used; trimethylol propane is one (Desmodur TH). These products are not completely free of uncombined diisocyanate. However, recently, Bayer claims to have produced a product that contains only 0.1 per cent free diisocyanate. Combinations of polyesters with these partially reacted diisocyanates represent much of the German art of forming lacquers which has been transmitted to us through Mobay. A good example of this technique is the following:

40 parts Desmophen 1100 ⎤
20 parts of ethyl acetate ⎥
20 parts of butyl acetate ⎥ Part A
20 parts of toluene ⎦

is mixed with 90 parts of Desmodur TH in ethyl acetate-toluene solution (50 per cent). The lacquer dries after about 3 hours and is completely hardened after 4 to 5 days. Curing may be accelerated by heating to 150°C. This improves the properties of the lacquer.

The next step in overcoming the difficulties of using raw diisocyanate is to prolong the pot life of the lacquer mixture or to make a one-component system. This leads to the use of hindered (or disguised) diisocyanate. The polyester and hindered diisocyanate are dissolved in a solvent, and do not react until the solution is applied to a surface, which is heated to liberate the diisocyanate. The material used to protect the diisocyanate must be either highly volatile or easily decomposed to volatile compounds. Malonic and acetoacetic esters belong to the latter category. However, a volatile compound is preferred, such as phenol. Rather than forming the diphenyl urethane of tolylene diisocyanate, it is preferable to form the triphenyl urethane of Desmodur TH. Here, a solution of phenol in ethyl acetate is added to a similar solution of Desmodur TH in an equivalent (or slight excess) of phenol. The resulting solution is heated to 100°C for several hours, until the addition of aniline to a diluted solution of the reaction in acetone shows no precipitate. This product is especially useful for wire coatings. The use of free diisocyanate formulations led to a constant increase in the viscosity of the lacquer with the result that the layers on the wire increased in thickness during the run of a given blend. To solve this problem, the above triphenyl urethane one-component system was devised. Urethane coatings on wire are particularly valuable because no stripping of the wire is needed before soldering. At temperatures above 250°C, reversion to volatile products occurs. Hence, coatings can be removed with a hot soldering iron. They can also be removed by dipping them in a solder bath, which results in a clean surface. The use of hindered diisocyanates eliminates the irritation and pot-life problems.

The German technology brought to the United States by

the Mobay Chemical Company may best be summarized by two technical papers given by their personnel at the isocyanate symposia in 1956. Similar to the Desmophens, the Mobay system is based on the Multrons, which are their polyesters. (See Table 8.1).

TABLE 8.1. POLYESTER RESINS FOR URETHANE COATINGS

Multron	Avg. Per Cent Hydroxyl	Branching	Major Field of Application
R-2	12.0	Very high	Wire coatings
R-4	8.2	High	Anti-corrosion coatings
R-10	6.4	Moderate	Anti-corrosion and general-purpose coatings
R-12	5.0	Slight	General-purpose coatings and rubber coatings
R-16	1.2	None	Rubber coatings
R-22	4.5	Moderate	Exterior coatings—all types

These resins are reacted with Mondur C which is the same as Desmodur TH, and Mondur S, which is its triphenyl urethane. In addition, tolylene diisocyanate may be used, but it is not preferred. A variety of films are now available which may be formed by a four-fold variation, according to the following system:

1. Type of isocyanate
2. Type of polyester
3. Ratio of isocyanate to hydroxyl
4. Method of cure

Table 8.1 shows the effect of varying the polyester. In addition, blends of these polyesters may be used in special cases to improve flexibility, etc. The other factors will be briefly discussed. It should be pointed out here that German experience underlines this art.

One of the variables mentioned above is the ratio of iso-cyanate equivalents to hydroxyl equivalents. It is easily

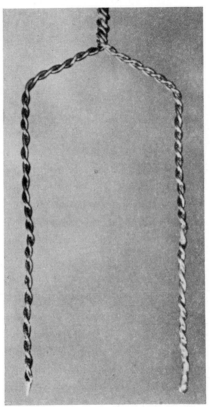

(Courtesy of Mobay Chemical Co.)

Figure 8.1. Conventional "solderable" wire (left) and wire coated with a urethane made from Mobay Chemical Company's "Mondur" isocyanates and "Multron" polyesters, both of which have been dipped into 360°C molten solder for 5 seconds. The urethane-coated wire is uniformly wet by the solder while the conventional "solderable" wire is merely coated with individual drops of solder.

shown that, as the latter ratio is increased, the hardness of the film increases, while the elongation is decreased. This would follow, since any excess isocyanate reacts to form cross-linking bonds in the form of allophanate groups. A better way to illustrate the cross-linking is to study the chemical resistance of urethane coatings.

TABLE 8.2. EFFECT OF POLYESTER AND NCO/OH RATIOS ON CHEMICAL RESISTANCE OF URETHANE COATINGS

| Multron | NCO/OH | Condition of Coatings After 2 Months Exposure | | |
		Benzene	Carbon Tetrachloride	Hexane
R-4	1.0	Excellent	Excellent	Excellent
R-10	1.0	Wrinkled	Wrinkled	Excellent
R-12	1.0	Wrinkled	Wrinkled	Excellent
R-10	1.5	Soft	Excellent	Excellent
R-12	1.5	Soft	Wrinkled	Excellent
R-10	1.7	Excellent	Excellent	Excellent
R-12	1.7	Soft	Soft	Excellent

All the coatings in Table 8.2 were air-dried for 10 days before being tested. It should be noted that the higher the initial branching in the resin, the better the resistance exhibited. Thus, R-4 is superior to R-10, and to R-12. It should also be noted that an increase in NCO/OH ratio improved the quality of the film. However, the type of resin originally used apparently sets a limit as to how much a film can be improved.

The last variable is the type of cure. The two-component urethane systems, air dry to give coatings with properties formerly associated only with baked coatings. Furthermore, baking the urethane coatings enhances their properties even more.

TABLE 8.3. EFFECT OF CONDITIONS ON PROPERTIES
OF URETHANE COATINGS

Multron	NCO/OH	Sward Hardness* Air Cure**	Bake***	Reverse Impact in Lbs. Air Cure	Bake
R-4	1.5	62	78	4	40
R-10	1.5	62	72	50	160
R-12	1.5	50	76	160	160

* Plate Glass—100.
** 10 days before test.
*** ½ hour at 300°F; then 3 days aging before test.

Table 8.3 is self-explanatory. The films exhibit an excellent increase in both hardness and toughness.

A successful field is that of wire coatings, which employs the very highly branched polyester Multron R-2. A typical formulation is:

2 parts—Mondur S
1 part —Multron R-2

dissolved at 30 per cent solids in a 2:1 ratio of high-flash naphtha to cresylic acid. The coating may be cured in a fraction of a minute at 600 to 700°F, after being applied by means of metal wiper dies. The film is resistant to solvents, water and abrasion, and has good flexural qualities. Typical electrical properties are given in Table 8.4.

TABLE 8.4. TYPICAL ELECTRICAL PROPERTIES OF URETHANE
ENAMELED WIRE

Property	Temperature °C 25°	75°	125°
Dielectric strength A.C. V/mil	5600	4400	3700
Resistivity ohm - cm	10^{16}	10^{15}	10^{13}
Dielectric constant	4.3	4.2	4.6
Loss factor, tan delta	0.01	0.01	0.04

In addition, excellent water resistance is shown by the small drop in dielectric strength from 5,000 to 3,800 V/mil after 30 weeks immersion in water at 20°C. The ease with which these coated wires can be soldered is another important advantage.

In addition to the polyesters, the Germans investigated other polyhydroxyl materials for use in coatings. One of these is the saponified copolymer of vinyl chloride and vinyl acetate. A suggested application is to use hindered diisocyanate to cross-link the copolymer. It is claimed that an elastic, scratch-proof and chemical-resistant film can be produced from a saponified copolymer of 80 parts vinyl chloride and 20 parts vinyl acetate reacted with 5 per cent of the hindered diisocyanate of hexamethylene diisocyanate and acetoacetic ester. The mixture is stable under 90°C to water and alcohol; but at 130°C, after removal of the solvent, dissociation of the addition product produces free diisocyanate for cross-linking, forming an insoluble lacquer coating. Other suggested hydroxyl compounds are cellulosic plastics, such as benzyl cellulose, alkyd modified phenolic resins and polyester oxygen rich xylene formaldehyde resins such as Desmophen 300. In all cases, the resulting films exhibited excellent adhesion to surfaces and high gloss. Furthermore, flexibility, abrasion resistance, and chemical resistance could be varied over a wide range. An interesting sidelight on the use of these lacquers has recently been found in the furniture field. The fast drying (or cure) of these materials to a tough, scratch-resistant and glossy film is excellent, but how can one retouch or refinish faulty work? It would be necessary to sand it down to the bare wood, which means refinishing an entire panel. A suggested way of getting around this, is first to apply a conventional lacquer to the piece of furniture, followed by an insoluble, synthetic top coat. The upper surface can then be scratched and treated with solvents, which will cut the lower layer and permit easy removal of the lacquer.

Another isocyanate coating suggested as a result of the German experimentation is the so-called "urethane oils." For this coating, various quantities of diisocyanates (one was chlorophenylene) were reacted with mono- and diglycerides of linseed oil. The products were supposedly equivalent to or superior to boiled linseed oil. The films of the urethane oils dried hard in a few hours, had more elasticity, better water resistance, but poorer light fastness. They believed that this was an excellent means of improving poor drying oils. On the other hand, the English found that this picture was far too rosy. They encountered gel formation early in their work, especially with dehydrated castor oil. To a large extent, they felt that this was due to the non-removal of some hydroxyl groups resulting from incomplete dehydration. Aliphatic diisocyanates (hexamethylene) were of too low a reactivity to be usable. Using chlorophenylene diisocyanate and linseed-oil mixed glycerides, they were able to make certain urethane oils. They found that increased amounts of diisocyanate improved drying time and resistance properties. The urethane oils exhibited somewhat inferior brushing properties and rather poor flow compared to long-oil alkyd. When theoretical diisocyanate was used, the product was superior to a high-class alkyd in drying speed, film hardness and water resistance, but showed poor color, increased after-yellowing, and inferior glow. All urethane oils showed a tendency to gel. What is surprising from the English work is the poor durability. Clear urethane oil varnishes were poorer in durability than alkyd varnishes. They were definitely inferior in gloss retention, chalking and color retention. It was felt that these results revealed the need for much more investigation.

Representative of some of the American experimentation

along the line of polyester-diisocyanates adducts is the work done by Reilly and Orchin, of the University of Cincinnati, in which the excellent abrasion resistance of polyurethane coatings was utilized in a fairly novel way. It has been found that the leading edges of high-speed aircraft wings are rapidly eroded by flight through a moderate storm. Under simulated conditions, an aluminum panel specimen, traveling at 500 miles per hour, in a rainfall of 1 inch per hour, will be roughened considerably in 5 to 10 minutes. Pitting is found in 15 minutes, and the corrosion rate increases till complete erosion occurs. It was decided that a strong elastic material would prevent this by absorbing the energy of impact. Literature search indicated that the polyurethanes would work, and their reports verified this.

The authors made polyesters of ethylene glycol and adipic acid in order to obtain hydroxyl-rich products with molecular weights about 3,000. These were reacted with an excess of tolylene diisocyanate to form adduct with about 65 per cent excess isocyanate. Ethanolamine was used to cure the resulting resin, using 75 to 100 per cent of that necessary to react with the free isocyanate groups. The published report was a preliminary one, but it showed the potential inherent in polyurethane coatings. By brushing on acetone-chlorobenzene solutions (containing all ingredients) they built up a layer of 0.010-0.015 inch. This was cured at 120°C for 2 hours, after preliminary air drying. After standing for several days, it was tested by the rain-erosion test. No essential wear occurred in the coating until 434 minutes had elapsed, except for a small pinhole which developed at the 294 minute mark. In contrast, a neoprene coating lasted only 56 minutes.

Nature has provided us with a cheap hydroxyl-rich branched polyester; namely, castor oil. The fatty acids of this oil contain about 85 per cent ricinoleic acid, which is

12-hydroxy oleic acid. Thus, the glyceride may be idealized as a trihydroxy polyol with a molecular weight of roughly 1000. Diisocyanate can be used to cross-link with this polyol, forming high molecular weight polymers that have many useful applications in commerce. National Aniline Corporation has revealed that one of these uses may be in the field of coatings. It has been shown that castor oil—diisocyanate adducts (or prepolymers)—can be cured with lead and cobalt driers to yield abrasion and chemical resistant coatings with excellent adhesion to most substrates. Using the molar ratio of 3 moles of diisocyanate to 1 mole of castor oil, clear coatings were made and compared to an alkyd resin.

TABLE 8.5. PROPERTIES OF DIISOCYANATE—CASTOR OIL
CLEAR COATINGS

Property	TDI—Castor Oil (on Steel)	MDI—Castor Oil (on Steel)	Medium Oil Length Alkyd
Abrasion index (mg loss—1000 cycles) (1000 g load cs-17 Wheel)	50	15	100
Sward hardness	10	17	
Chemical resistance Time to failure			
Boiling water	100 hrs	120 hrs	
25% sulfuric acid	>3 months	>3 months	
5% caustic soda	>2 months	>2 months	0.5 hrs
5% hypochlorite	200 hrs	200 hrs	
"Nacconol SL" solution	>4 months	>4 months	
1% citric acid	>1 month	>1 month	
Mineral spirits	>1 month	>1 month	

Similiar results were obtained with pigmented systems. However, the stability of pigment systems is not as good as unpigmented ones. It was interesting to note that, in these studies, the 3:1 molar ratio produced the hardest coatings. There was a rapid loss in hardness with either an increase or decrease in the diisocyanate molar ratio.

Several applications in the coatings field were used to illustrate the excellence of these relatively cheap products. Polyester-fiber glass drier pans are used in their chemical plants to dry various materials of different degrees of acidity, alkalinity and salt content. After being used for a short period, severe corrosion was noted. Application of the MDI castor oil prepolymer gave essentially complete protection. The same coating on filter press plates improved considerably the life of these structural units against 5 per cent caustic soda at 180°C and cold mineral acids. This coating was found to protect steel racks used in a 170 to 180°F steam chamber (to cure cement blocks). These had been replaced at the rate of five times a year, but upon application of the coating no corrosion was noticed after six months of service. This coating was also found to produce a durable moisture barrier on concrete. It gave full protection and no significant wear was noticed in the period of a winter. Before application, salt water would percolate through concrete cracks, causing trouble. These few examples illustrate the possibilities inherent in this relatively cheap coating material.

9. TEXTILE APPLICATIONS

As pointed out previously, the initial impetus which led to the investigation and application of the polyurethanes in Germany was the desire to create a fiber which would be of the nylon type. The simple operation of being able to combine two reagents to form high-molecular weight polymers, without the production difficulties involved in removing traces of water of reaction required to produce the condensation necessary to attain the proper high-molecular weight essential for nylon, was another inducement. A fiber, "Perlon U," was developed, which, in several respects, was superior to nylon. However, although much interest has been displayed both here and abroad in this field, there is little or no production of this product at present. During the war, approximately 25 tons per month of "Perlon U" was spun by the hot-melt method and cold drawn for use in the manufacture of parachute fabrics. The trend is toward the use of this thermoplastic extrusion material for bristles because of its higher rigidity and lower water absorption than nylon. Because of this latter use, and the interest displayed in the possibilities of these fibers, an attempt will be made here to cover the field as broadly as possible.

The original investigation was directed toward the production of high-molecular weight linear polymers by the addition of diisocyanates to diamines or glycols to form the corresponding polyureas and polyurethanes. It was then discovered that the reaction with diamines led to insoluble, infusible and strongly hydrophilic polymers, not suitable for either fibers or plastics. Experimentation showed that aliphatic components such as the glycols were more useful, as the introduction of aromatic rings in the polyurethane chain produced brittleness and poor fiber-forming properties. Furthermore, secondary and tertiary hydroxyl groups lowered the melting point of the resultant polyurethane too much, and also decreased the thermostability markedly. Polyurethanes with side chains have lower strengths and excessive solubility in organic solvents. The final form of polyurethane developed was made from primary diols of three carbons or more (the polyurethanes of ethylene glycol decomposed upon melting, with the formation of gas) and similarly constituted aliphatic diisocyanates.

A series of polyurethanes was made from the various glycols and diisocyanates. Table 9.1 shows some of the more interesting and commercially feasible ones. It was found that fibers could easily be formed from these polymers. Data from this table, as well as other experimental work, clearly showed that odd carbon chains decreased the melting point of the plastic. The highest melting polyurethane was formed using two four-carbon chains; however, it was not used because of the difficulty of producing pure tetramethylene diisocyanate of the desired purity. Instead, the polyurethane made from butanediol-1,4 and hexamethylene diisocyanate-1,6 was used; it was called "Perlon U." But it must be remembered that, potentially, tetramethylene diisocyanate would be cheaper to produce (via acetylene chemistry), and would make a better fiber.

"Perlon U" may be prepared in several ways. The following method is suggested: One mole of hexamethylene diisocyanate is added to one mole of butanediol-1,4 dissolved in monochlorbenzene. The reaction is strongly exothermic; about 208 Cal/kg of polyurethane is liberated. After one hour, the polyurethane separates out as a fine sandy powder in yields of 98 per cent or so. Molecular weights of about 10,000 may be obtained, which are within the proper range for spinning. The precipitation from a solvent during preparation eliminates a low molecular portion, as well as byproducts, leaving a fairly sharp molecular distribution much

TABLE 9.1. MELTING POINTS OF POLYURETHANES

Number of Carbons in Diisocyanate	Glycol	Melting Point (°C)
4	4	190
4	6	180
4	10	170
5	4	159
6	3	167
6	4	183
6	5	159
6	9	147
8	4	160
8	6	153
12	12	128

finer than that of nylon. Furthermore, it should be noted that the condensation is much simpler in principle than that for nylon. The raw materials must be of the highest purity to eliminate the possibility of the presence of chain breakers. The molecular weight can be varied by adjusting the physical factors of the reaction, such as temperature, use of a better solvent, etc., as well as such chemical factors as variations in mole ratios and the presence of monofunctional compounds to act as chain breakers. The polyurethanes are not too stable, thermally speaking; they tend to decompose into their original components at about 220°C and, hence, it is probably impossible to process them if they have melting points above 230°C (range of nylon). However, "Perlon U" has a much lower melting point (183°C) which is somewhat too low for many textile applications. It has a very sharp melting point due to its narrower molecular distribution. The spinning of "Perlon U" is somewhat more difficult than other synthetic fibers. Its softening point is about 170°C and, hence, quite close to its melting point; its melts are quite thin. In the orientation of "Perlon U," precautions must be taken to prevent crystallization. This latter operation increases the density of the plastic from 1.18 to 1.21.

"Perlon U" is a rather stiff fiber; it is suitable as a substitute for horsehair and for use in specialized industrial applications. The polyurethanes are superior to nylon fibers in electric qualities, weatherproofness, resistance to mineral acids and hydrophobic qualities. In the laboratory, "Perlon U" exhibits tensile strengths up to 8g/denier, as compared to 5.3g/denier for commercial nylon and 3.5g/denier for natural silks. Some uses recommended for these fibers are filter cloths, protective clothing (resistant to acids and mustard gas), driving belts, ropes, cable insulation, fishing implements, etc. However, they are not suitable for underwear and hosiery. In general, due to its hardness, wire-like elasticity and insensitivity to water, "Perlon U" is most suitable for bristles and extrusions (sold as "Igamid U"). Though the polyurethanes resemble nylon in many of their working properties, such as hot water set, their dyeing properties are quite dissimilar. They may be dyed only with cellulose acetate dyes and not with acid dyestuffs. At present the simple linear polyurethanes, such as "Perlon U," are not commercially feasible due to their relatively low melting points and higher cost than such synthetic fibers as nylon and "Dacron."

As mentioned in Chapter 2, a plastic similar to "Perlon U" can also be made via the chlorocarbonic ester route. In this case, one mole of 1,4-butanediol bis-chlorocarbonic acid ester is reacted with one mole of hexamethylenediamine to produce a very soft "Perlon U." The so-called "softness" is due to the lower uniformity of polymerization and, hence, a wider thermoplastic range. Attempts have been made to improve the resulting lower melting point by incorporating tri- and tetra-functional compounds. Thus, for 21.5 parts of the above bis ester, 0.2 part of trimethylol propane trichlorocarbonic acid ester is used. The product has a melting point above 180°C. Some of the diamine may be replaced by triamines and tetramines. In this way, products melting above 200°C have been obtained. Essentially, the plastics produced by this series of reactions are similar to those made by the diisocyanate reactions.

Perlons have a glossy appearance, and a very low degree of moisture absorption and moisture regain. Because of the latter, they have a somewhat cold feel, as well as a harsh and wiry hand. Several attempts have been made to overcome these disadvantages. Patent literature reveals that treatment of these filaments with formaldehyde or formaldehyde-producing materials will substantially eliminate the above undesirable properties. There is an increase in melting point and normal moisture content or moisture regain. A soft silky appearance and very desirable hand results. Thus, a linear polyurethane made from tetramethylene diisocyanate and butanediol-1,4 (melting point −208°C)* was immersed in the following solution:

Formaldehyde (40% aqueous)	4.5	by weight
Hydrochloric acid	0.12	" "
Methyl alcohol	3.2	" "

for one hour at 60°C. After washing and drying, the polymer was found to have a melting point above 300°C. The

---

* Note the melting point is higher than that found in the German investigations, indicating that probably the raw materials used in this work were of higher purity.

hand changed from a hard and wiry one to a soft and silky one—due mainly to an increase in moisture regain properties. Similar results were obtained at the other end of the pH scale. Replacement of the acid in the above solution by 0.01 part of sodium hydroxide, but using the same physical technique, also produced a filament with a soft hand. The melting point was only 270°C. Thus, it is possible to alter the linear polyurethanes to produce textile fibers rather than just industrially valuable products.

As early as 1920, attempts were made to modify cellulosic materials with isocyanates to improve their properties. A phenyl carbamic ester of cellulose was patented as a possible substitute for cellulose esters. The procedure was quite cumbersome; dried cotton cellulose was reacted with phenyl isocyanate in pyridine. In the latter half of the 1920's, a series of patents was issued covering the formation and use of nitrogen-substituted cellulose thiourethanes as fibers, films, etc. This was interesting because it disclosed another method of preparation in which an alkaline solution of sodium cellulose xanthate (viscose) was reacted with chloroacetic acid to form cellulose xanthacetate sodium salt. This salt, when stirred with aniline and other amines (primary and secondary), forms the corresponding cellulose thiourethane and splits out sodium thioglycollate. The thiourethane precipitated out of solution and was recovered in the conventional manner. In order to make fibers, advantage was taken of the fact that the thiourethanes were usually soluble in dilute alkali. Hence, an alkaline solution could be spun in the usual manner, using precipitating baths of acidic materials. Shiny, transparent and flexible films, resistant to water, were obtained by solvent casting. An aqueous solution of pyridine of 70 to 80 per cent strength was suggested as the solvent. Recently, these products were prepared by a variation of the above method and more intensely evaluated. The sodium salt of cellulose xanthate was precipitated with zinc salts to form zinc cellulose xanthate. The precipitates were slurried at room temperature for several days in dilute solutions of amines in water to form the precipitates of the corresponding thiourethanes. Fibers could be spun from these in much the same way as described above. Wool type dyes could be used to dye them. The striking characteristic of these fibers is their resistance to hydrochloric acid.

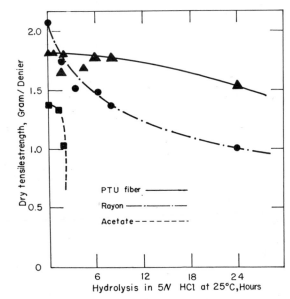

Figure 9.1. Effect of 5N hydrochloric acid at 25°C on tensile strength. (*Courtesy Industrial & Engineering Chemistry*, **49**, p. 74, 1957.)

The superiority of cellulose phenyl thiourethane (PTU) over rayon and cellulose acetate is apparent. This latter work, from the laboratories of American Viscose, represents a good comparative study of these cellulosic derivatives with rayon and cellulose acetate.

The use of diisocyanates as cross-linking agents for commercial cellulose acetate, which always has some free hydroxyl groups, appears feasible. This has the effect of increasing the melting point of cellulose ester and decreasing its solubility in various solvents. Of course, the addition of diisocyanate to a solution of the cellulose acetate would only cause a precipitate of the cross-linked polymer, requiring the use of blocked diisocyanate compounds. Derivatives of phenol, acetoacetic ester and malonic ester have been used with the various diisocyanates. Three to 20 per cent of these derivatives (based on the plastic) are dissolved in the spinning solution. After the fiber is formed in the usual manner, it is heated to 150 to 160°C. The blocked diisocyanates dissociate, liberating diisocyanate, which reacts with the fiber to cross-link. This method is applicable to other cellulose esters.

A drawback of many of the uses for cotton and regenerated cellulose fibers is the fact that they cannot be dyed with the so-called "acid-wool" dyestuffs. A good example is the desire to dye blends of these fibers with wool to the same tone. The process of altering the cellulosic materials so they can be dyed with the above dyes is called "animalizing." Among the better animalizing agents are the polyurethanes and, preferably, the polyureas. This is about the only use for which the polyureas have been found valuable. The preferred method is to form the resin, and suspend it into the cellulose spinning bath with the aid of emulsifiers, mechanical dispersions, etc. After spinning in the usual manner, the resulting fibers can be dyed with acid-wool dyes; they exhibit excellent fastness properties. An example of such a polyurea is made from:

> 100   parts—*p*-cyclohexylene diisocyanate
> 61.3 parts—*p*-cyclohexylene diame.

Solution dipping is another method. If cotton is immersed in a 5 per cent solution of a polyurethane made as follows:

    70.8 parts—diphenylene diisocyanate
    44.9 parts—β, β'-di(hydroxyl ethyl) cyclohexylamine
     5.4 parts—butylene glycol-1,4

in methyl formamide for a period of 1 hour at 40 to 50°C, it can be dyed with acid-wool dyes. Hence, the process of animalizing may be performed either in the spinning bath or as a finish after this operation. Extension to cellulose acetate and other synthetic fibers has been proposed.

A recent process has been described which makes it possible to dye plastics with acid dyes to satisfactory shades under usual wool-dyeing conditions. In one case the cellulose thiourethanes mentioned above were utilized. These were further acetylated, and the products dissolved in spinning dope solutions of such plastics as cellulose acetate, in proportion of 10 to 30 per cent. The resultant fibers were dyeable with acid dyes. Similar plastics, such as polystyrene and copolymers of acrylonitrile, can be made to dye under the same conditions. A polyurethane with a tertiary amine in the repeating unit can also be used in a similar manner and will be better than one with the tertiary amine missing. The polyurethane must be made by the chlorocarbonic ester method because a diisocyanate cannot be made with a tertiary amine in the molecule.

It has been suggested that fibers treated with isocyanate materials in the finishing process will tend to be waterproof and non-shrinkable. Most emphasis has been placed on the use of the bisulfite addition product of higher aliphatic isocyanate such as stearyl in conjunction with other waterproofing agents—paraffin wax, aluminum and zicronium salts, etc. In the second method, emulsions of the lower active aliphatic mono- and diisocyanates such as higher aliphatic isocyanates and hexamethylene diisocyanate are used. The third method uses solutions of various mono- and diisocyanates in organic solvents; here, aromatic compounds may also be used. These three methods were studied in detail. After the various treatments the viscose fibers were reacted with cuprammonium solution to remove unreacted cellulose. The last method (solvent treatment) merely coated the surface, but did not penetrate deeply. The emulsion method enables the isocyanate to penetrate the fiber and produce an insoluble central region. Addition of urea produced a more solid central core. The bisulfite addition product completely penetrates the fiber uniformly. Again, the presence of urea aids the process. It is surprising that even the solvent method imparts a high degree of wash resistance on the finish. Though the patent literature contains a great deal of work done along these lines, there is apparently no commercial development being done at present.

10. MISCELLANEOUS

The method of potting, or the encapsulation of electronic components, has become widespread in the industry. The advantages are manifold.

(1) Rigid location of components in relation to each other.

(2) Increased electrical resistance between adjacent components.

(3) Increased resistance to humidity.

(4) Increased resistance to vibration.

(5) Increased chemical resistance.

(6) Improved heat transfer.

Both solid and foamed polyurethanes (see Chapter 3) have shown excellent merit in potting. The role of non-foamed polyurethanes will be discussed here. These have been suggested and proved successful; for example, Army and Navy specifications have been fulfilled.

The Plastics Laboratory of Princeton University studied the use of solid polyurethanes under a Defense Department contract, and reported on them as early as June, 1949. It recommended the use of castor oil tolylene diisocyanate adduct modified with glycols. The reasons for choosing castor oil as the base for the potting compound are given in Chapter 4. After studying the effects of molar ratios of tolylene diisocyanate to castor oil, and of various glycols and glycerine on the electrical and mechanical properties of resulting resins, this laboratory recommended the following molar ratios:

Castor oil—1.66

Tolylene diisocyanate—3.50-4.00

2 Ethyl hexanediol-1,3—1.00

It was suggested that small quantities of Sylon RD-602 (ditertiary butoxy diamine silane) be used as the curing agent. The quantities required do not, apparently, have any effect on the physical and electrical properties of the final polymers.

The above polyurethane resin was a hard, brittle, yet fairly thermoplastic material with the lowest loss qualities. One possible drawback was the fact that it is difficult to obtain bubble-free products, regardless of cure conditions. Cures at room temperature with Sylon are comparable to uncatalyzed cures at 40 and 85°C. The cured resins looked and felt like clear rubber, but they did not bounce; however, they did absorb shock and damp vibrations and noises. When poured into a mold, the polyurethane will take the shape of the mold, adhere well, show negligible shrinkage on gelation, and will not cause internal shearing among the components. The following values, obtained with various samples, are typical of its good electrical properties.

Volume resistivity—$>10^7$ megohms/in.

Surface resistivity—>15.7 x 10^6 megohms

Dielectric strengths—order of 400 volts/mil (bubbles caused premature breakdown)

Arc resistance—about 150 seconds; melts first (decomposes), and then burns.

The mechanical properties are also good, but here again bubbles may cause failure. Its chemical resistance to caustic alkalies and mineral acids is good, as is its heat resistance. Good solvents, such as toluene and carbon tetrachloride, will extract small quantities of non-volatiles. From the above data, the experimentalists concluded that these resins might make excellent potting compounds.

In order to study this matter more carefully, they potted several transformers, and subjected the final encapsulations to Army and Navy Specifications JAN-T-27. The five-cycle test showed little effect on the electrical properties. After 5 cycles, the potted transformers were immersed in saturated salt solution at room temperature for 66 hours, with little effect on the electrical properties.

National Aniline has recently suggested tentative potting compounds based on castor oil and tolylene diisocyanate, as well as other diisocyanates, such as diphenyl methane; it has also suggested replacing the castor oil with low-branched polyesters, such as those used to make flexible foamed urethanes. Two sample preparations will be given as examples:

Preparation 1. 200 grams of diphenyl methane diisocyanate is added to 246 grams of dry castor oil, with constant agitation, holding the temperature at 70°C (about one hour). The product is degassed by heating at 100°C under a vacuum of less than 5-mm absolute pressure for 30 minutes (until bubbling ceases). The vacuum is broken by bleeding in dry nitrogen. The resin is cooled to 70°C, and 4 grams of "Quadrol" (Wyandotte Chemical) is added. Vacuum is again applied for about 5 minutes, until bubbling ceases, and it is then released as before. The resin may now be poured in the mold and cured at 100°C. The product requires about 18 hours to set and should have good toughness and resilience properties.

Preparation 2. 90 grams of tolylene diisocyanate (80/20 isomer ratio) is added to 412 grams of "Paraplex U-148" (Rohm and Haas) with constant agitation, at 70°C (about

30 minutes). The mixture is kept at this temperature another 30 minutes, and then degassed at 65 to 75°C, under a vacuum of 5-mm absolute pressure until bubbling ceases. A period of 30 minutes is required. After this step, dry nitrogen is used to release the vacuum. 15 grams of "Quadrol" is stirred in well for 2 minutes. A second degassing is done at 75 to 80°C. The bubble-free resin is poured into the mold and cured at 100°C. A set is obtained in about 18 hours. The casting will be clear, elastic and resilient.

The molds may be coated with silicone release agents if removal is required. In addition to "Quadrol," which is a propylene oxide addition product of ethylenediamine, the use of ethyl diethanol amine is suggested to speed up the cure. Other low-branched polyesters besides "Paraplex U148" may be used. The hardness of the final product can be varied by the amount of branching.

Most of the isocyanate products are formed by the reaction with hydroxyl compounds; other active hydrogen compounds are of minor consideration. However, the one field in which the use of amine compounds is of prime interest, is that of tanning hides. It was noted that application of the urea-forming reaction with isocyanate could be used to harden gelatin, and to increase the fastness to moisture and boiling water of casein and wool. Here, the diisocyanates cross-link the protein chains. In the tanning process it is important that the tanning agent should penetrate the hide, not merely harden the surface. This is similar to "animalizing viscose" (Chapter 9). The Germans found that hexamethylene diisocyanate is an excellent tanning agent for hides, and sold it under the name of "Gerbstoff H." Because of its comparatively low activity, the diisocyanate could be emulsified and used without too much loss of activity. The suggested method of application was to emulsify 3 parts of diisocyanate with 0.5 part of "Emulphor O" in 50 parts of water; this was applied to 100 parts of hide in a rolling drum. A chamois-like leather is obtained in a period of a few hours. It is probable that two reactions take place: (1) polyurea forms within the hide, and, (2) the protein chains become cross-linked. Thick hides can be thoroughly tanned. It is claimed that this process is cheaper than the metallic salt methods because of lower costs of manipulation.

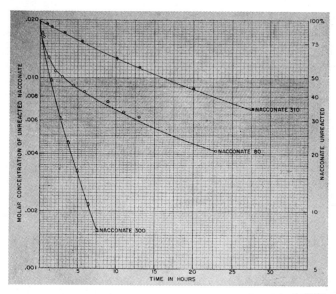

Figure 10.1. Reactivity of "Nacconates 80," 300 and 310 with 2-ethylhexanol at 28°C. (*Courtesy National Aniline Co.*)

In the United States, the proposed diisocyanate for tanning is 3,3'-dimethyl diphenylmethane-4,4'-diisocyanate. As will be discussed in Chapter 11, hexamethylene diisocyanate is a bad irritant. It is not being manufactured in the United States but may be obtained from Germany. Dimethyl diphenylmethane diisocyanate is a low-melting solid (solidification point 31.4°C) and, hence, can easily be emulsified for use. Anionic and nonionic emulsifiers should be used in neutral or weakly acidic solutions. Its vapor pressure is quite low under ordinary working conditions (2 mm at 200°C). Thus, it is much less of an irritant than hexamethylene diisocyanate and even may be considered relatively harmless; care must be taken, however, to wash off any contamination on the skin. The emulsified diisocyanate is quite stable, and under normal working conditions can be used without much loss of activity before the tanning action.

It may be noted from Figure 10.1 that the reactions of tolylene diisocyanate (80/20 isomer ratio) with 2-ethylhexanol will pass the half-way mark in 3 hours; that of the diisocyanate in question takes 16 hours. It is interesting to note that the diisocyanate without the two methyl groups, namely, diphenylmethane diisocyanate, requires less than 1.5 hours. Hence, it can be seen that the sterically hindered diisocyanate is weakly active and will be carried into the hide, tanning it thoroughly.

11. HANDLING OF DIISOCYANATES

Because the tolylene diisocyanates are much the most important of the diisocyanates from a commercial standpoint, handling, safety problems, and precautions to be taken are highly important. The other diisocyanates should be considered in relation to the tolylene diisocyanates in these respects. The tolylene diisocyanates cannot be regarded as toxic materials, but rather as irritants to the mucous membranes, particularly of the respiratory system and eyes. Studies made on animals, both here and in Europe, have revealed that the oral toxicity of TDI is quite low. Furthermore, subcutaneous injections of the order of 10 to 500 mg/kg of body weight showed an absence of any toxic symptoms. Application of tolylene diisocyanate to the skin produced minor irritation, except to the eye. The most serious effect on test animals is the irritation caused by inhalation.

The clinical results reported by several European countries (France, Sweden and Germany) were similar to those obtained by animal tests. Despite adverse working conditions, no case of skin disorder has been discovered there. Evidence definitely proved that tolylene diisocyanates are respiratory irritants. Most of the cases encountered were caused by the use of tolylene diisocyanate in lacquer formulations, where the patients were spray painting and ventilation was inadequate. Here, the irritation to the patient was further aggravated by the employment of irritating solvents in the spray process. A general pattern of asthmatic bronchitis developed. Throat irritation and coughing resulted, followed by short breath and a general asthmatic condition. However, the patients recovered when they were removed from the source of irritation. Many of them, however, may have had developed an increased sensitivity to tolylene diisocyanates. It must be kept in mind that the above represent acute cases of irritation.

The first precaution in any work involving diisocyanates is to examine the potential personnel, especially those who may come in contact with these chemicals in an uncombined state, for any previous history of asthma, bronchial lesions or any other respiratory disorders. If any of these conditions are found, the personnel in question should be rejected. Next, an adequate system of ventilation should be installed. A good starting point is to maintain a minimum linear air velocity under normal working conditions of at least 40 feet per minute. Using this base point, the air may be sampled during the various operations to see what the tolylene diisocyanate concentration is and the ventilation adjusted accordingly. The Mine Safety Company, of Pittsburgh, Pennsylvania, sells an air sampler for TDI which is constructed according to the recommendations of duPont. The latter company suggests that 0.1 ppm be used as a safe working level. 0.4 ppm has been found to be the lowest level that may be detected by odor. At 0.8 ppm, an appreciable odor may be noted; while at 0.5 ppm, irritation of the nose and throat will occur. These levels will vary greatly from person to person. They do indicate, however, that if TDI is noted, something should be done about it, especially if the condition persists. Proper protective equipment, such as goggles, should be worn when these chemicals are being handled. There is no reason to have any trouble with TDI if the above simple precautions are taken.

If a great deal of work is anticipated with diisocyanates, a physician should be alerted and any literature on the subject obtained in case of any emergency. A good reference is the HR-12 report of the Elastomers Division of duPont, entitled, "Safety and Handling Manual for Hylene Organic Isocyanates." If any emergency exists, such as spillage, etc., the solubility of TDI should be considered and an attempt made to counteract and destroy the diisocyanate. Alcohols (such as isopropanol) are good solvents and excellent deactivators for isocyanates; and, hence, whenever possible, should be used to wash down and decontaminate spillage. Water is immiscible with TDI and will not react too readily with it. Instead, it will tend to spread the diisocyanate and cause more harm. Aqueous solutions of alcohols with soap may be used to destroy and clean away TDI. If TDI gets into the eyes, thorough rinsing with water is suggested. The European practice is to use vegetable oils. A respirator, equipped with a cartridge recommended for use with organic chemical vapors, should be available. Proper ventilation is essential at all times.

As to the relative harmfulness of other diisocyanates, the question of volatility is most important. The aliphatic diisocyanates, such as hexamethylene diisocyanate, are usually much more volatile than tolylene diisocyanate and hence, much greater irritants. In addition, these have been claimed to have pathogenic properties and are believed to cause dermatitis. In fact, the production of hexamethylene diisocyanate has been suspended at times because of this. The aromatic diisocyanates are less volatile and, hence, less irritating than TDI. Apparently, the handling problem revolves around the volatility of the diisocyanate product. As a result, several addition products of TDI and other diisocyanates with polyols have been made available which have low amounts of free diisocyanate. A case in point is the product formed by one mole of hexanetriol and 3 moles of TDI. To illustrate the volatility problem further, a compound of 2,4-TDI reacted with water in the molar ratio of 2:1 will give a product where the 4 positions are joined on a urea linkage and the 2 positions are free. This product, sold as "Hylene TU," is a high melting solid (172 to 178°C); it is relatively non-irritating and can be handled with ordinary care. It is recommended for use as a urethane elastomer vulcanizer. Therefore, a good approximation of the irritation to be expected with a given diisocyanate product is its relative volatility, except for aliphatics, which act somewhat more so as irritants.

It must be remembered that tolylene diisocyanates have been used for many years by companies on both sides of the Atlantic without any lasting harmful effects to their personnel. The only record of any difficulty resulted from the use of spray lacquers in Europe. In all cases, extremely bad ventilation and the lack of masks were shown to be at fault. We have here a respiratory irritant and not a toxic chemical. Proper normal handling of a comparatively simple nature is all that is required.

BIBLIOGRAPHY

In addition to technical literature which may be obtained from the various raw material manufacturers and suppliers, the following literature references are suggested:

A. L. Allewelt, "Cellulose Phenyl Thiourethane Fibers," *Industrial & Engineering Chemistry*, **49**, 71-78 (1957).

A. L. Allewelt and W. R. Watt, "New Method for Preparing Cellulose Thiourethanes," *Industrial & Engineering Chemistry*, **49**, 68-70 (1957).

W. E. Allsebrook, "Isocyanates in Surface Coatings," *Paint Manufacture,* **25**, 459-61, 469 (1955).

Symposium on Isocyanate Polymers, American Chemical Society, Division of Paints, Plastics & Printing Ink Chemistry, Atlantic City, September 1956.

"Diisocyanate-Polyester Compounds," American Chemical Society—Rubber Division Library Bibliography #25—June 1955, University of Akron.

Anon., "Properties of Urethane Oils," *The Chemical Age*, **54**, 481-84 (1951).

O. Bayer, "Polyurethanes," *Modern Plastics,* **24**, 149-52, 250, 252, 254, 256, 258, 260, 262 (1947).

O. Bayer, "Das Di-Isocyanat-Polyadditions-Ver Fahren" (Polyurethane), *Angewandte Chemie*, **A59**, 257-72 (1942)—Fiat Review of German Science, 1939-1946—Preparative Organic Chemistry, Part III, pp. 303-352.

O. Bayer, E. Muller, S. Petersen, H. F. Piopenbrink and E. Windemuth, "New Types of Highly Elastic Substances," *Vulcollans-Rubber Chemistry and Technology,* **23**, 812-35 (1950)—translation from *Angewandte Chemie,* **62**, No. 3, 57-66 (1950).

J. Bjorksten, H. Toveyand, H. L. Dollard, Jr., "Polyurethane Resins," *Modern Plastics,* **31**, 143-146, 228-230, 233 (1954).

J. Brennan, "Some Uses of Polyurethanes in Electronics and Surface Coatings," *British Plastics,* **28**, 417-21 (1955).

J. K. Buxbaum, "Analytical Studies on the Aging of Isocyanate-Based Foams," *Analytical Chemistry,* **29,** 492-499 (1957).

"Development of Heat-Resistant, Foamed-in-Place Dielectric Core Materials for Sandwich Radomes," Cornell Aeronautical Laboratory PB 111692 (March 1954).

E. G. Corphey, "Isocyanate Elastomers," *British Plastics,* **27,** 407-409 (1954).

De Bell, Goggin and Gloor, "German Plastics Practise," Murray Printing Co., Cambridge, Mass. (1946).

G. H. Gates and W. M. Larson, "Polyurethane Rubber As A Material of Construction," *Mechanical Engineering,* **78,** 1016-1018 (1956).

Goodyear Aircraft Corporation, "Radome Materials Research and Fabrication Service," PB #110497.

Goodyear Aircraft Corporation, "Foaming in Place Alkyd Resins for Sandwich Radomes," PB #110498.

D. A. Harper, L. F. Smith, and H. G. White, "Some New Compositions Based on Condensation Rubbers," *Rubber Chemistry & Technology,* **23,** 608-14 (1950).

C. J. Harrington, "Polyurethane Foams," *S.P.E. Journal,* **12,** No. 10, 19-22 (1956).

"Polyurethanes," Harvard University Graduate School of Business Administration, April 30, 1956.

H. L. Heiss, J. H. Saunders, M. E. Morris, B. R. Davis and E. E. Hardy, "Preparation of Polymers from Diisocyanates and Polyols," *Industrial & Engineering Chemistry,* **46,** 1498-1503 (1954).

F. B. Hill, C. A. Young, J. A. Nelson and R. G. Arnold, "Urethane Rubber from a Polyether Glycol, Properties of Raw Polymer and Vulcanizates," *Industrial & Engineering Chemistry,* **48,** 927-929 (1956).

R. P. Hopkins, "Polyester-Urethane Foams," *Resin Review,* No. 15, 8-16 (July 1955).

G. M. Kline, "Plastics in Germany 1939-1945," *Modern Plastics,* **23,** 152A-P (1945).

Landells, "Resin Finishing of Textiles," *Journal of the Society of Dyers & Colourists,* **72,** 144-145 (1956).

"Castor Oil Polyurethanes and Applications as Potting Compounds," Plastics Laboratory, Princeton University, U.S.O.T.S. 9916S.

C. B. Reilly and M. Orchin, "Preparation and Properties of Polyurethane Coatings," *Industrial & Engineering Chemistry,* **48,** 59-63 (1956).

J. S. Rugg and G. W. Scott, "Urethane Rubber from a Polyether Glycol—Factors Influencing Processability," *Industrial & Engineering Chemistry,* **48,** 930-933 (1956).

K. Satterly, "Foamed Isocyanates," *Product Engineering,* 140-143 (February 1955).

J. H. Saunders and R. J. Slocombe, "The Chemistry of the Organic Isocyanates," *Chemical Review,* **43,** 203-218 (1948).

N. V. Seeger, T. G. Martin, E. E. Fauser, F. S. Farson, A. F. Finelli, and E. A. Sinclair, "Chemigum SL—An Elastomeric Polyester Urethane," **45,** 2538-42 (1953).

Isocyanate Symposium, October 23, 1956—Minneapolis, Minnesota, S.P.E. Upper Midwest Section.

"Urethane Plastics," A Staff Report, *Industrial & Engineering Chemistry,* **48,** 1383-1391.

"Isocyanate Resins for Coatings," Staff Report, *Paint & Varnish Production,* pp. 25-30, 70-71 (December 1955).

A. C. Stevenson, "Isocyanates," *Rubber Age,* **77,** No. 1, 63-68 (April 1955).

APPENDIX

DETERMINATION OF AMINE EQUIVALENT

(Pertinent analytic method not usually found in chemical books.)

Scope and Application:

1. This procedure is intended to determine the combining weight of any isocyanate containing material.

Summary of Method:

2. The isocyanate groups are reacted with di-*n*-butylamine to form a corresponding urea.

Definitions:

3. Amine equivalent: the number of grams of an isocyanate consumed by one gram mole of a secondary amine in the formation of the corresponding urea. (See #1 for alternate definition.)

Apparatus:

4. (a) 100 ml automatic burette with desiccant tubes.

(b) A 20 and 25 ml pipette conforming to National Bureau of Standards tolerances.

Reagents:

5. (a) Di-*n*-butylamine (2N): dilute 258 grams of redistilled di-*n*-butylamine with redistilled toluene to a total volume of one liter.

(b) Brom cresol green indicator: dissolve 1 gram of indicator in isopropanol to obtain a total volume of 100 mls. (NB. An alcoholic solution is recommended to give a sharper end point.)

(c) Approximately $N/2$ Hydrochloric acid solution (aqueous) standardized by accepted methods to $\pm$ 0.001N.

(d) Isopropyl alcohol (Technical grade, but alkaline free).

(e) Dry toluene.

Procedure:

6. (a) Selection of sample weight is based on the following table:

TABLE I

Anticipated Amine Equivalent	Sample Size (grams)	Tolerance (mg)
0-100	1-2	± 5
100-250	2-3	± 5
250-500	3-5	± 5
500-	5-7	±50

(b) Determination of amine equivalent: Weigh sample by difference into a clean and dry 500 cc Erlenmeyer flask. Pipette 25 ml of toluene into flask and dissolve sample, warming gently if necessary. (Do not boil!)

Pipette 20 ml of the 2N Di-*n*-butylamine solution into the flask and stopper. Swirl vigorously and let cool (10-20 minutes) to room temperature.

Add 100 ml of isopropanol, 10 drops Brom cresol green indicator solution, and titrate with $N/2$ HCl to a green to yellow end point.

A blank determination is run in exactly the same manner using all the reagents but omitting the sample.

Calculation:

7. The Amine equivalent is calculated by the following formula:

$$\frac{W}{(B\text{-}S) \times N} = \text{Amine Equivalent}$$

Where:
W—Sample weight in milligrams
B—Volume of HCl used in titrating blank
S—Volume of HCl used in titrating sample
N—Exact normality of the HCl solution

Precision:

8. (a) Repeatability: duplicate results by the same analyst should be considered suspect if they differ by more than 0.25% relative.

(b) Reproducibility: the average result reported by one laboratory should not be considered suspect unless it differs from that of another by more than 0.5% relative.

INDEX

Active hydrogen compound,
    definition of, 16
Adhesives, 124-133
  American techniques, 127
  castor-oil adducts, 133
  German techniques, 124
  methods of application, 130
"Adiprenes," 106, 118-123
Amine equivalent
  definition of, 39
  determination of, 171
  use in calculations, 39
"Animalizing agents," 154

Bayer, Otto, Dr., 5, 6, 26

Caprolactone, 98
  foams from, 99
Carwin Chemical Co., 10, 13
Castor oil
  adhesives, 133
  coatings, 144
  idealized structure, 57
  use in semi-rigid foams, 57
"Chemigum SL," 114, 116, 118
  aging study, 115
  characteristics of, 114
  preparation of, 114
Coatings, 134-146
  for airplane wing protection,
    144

castor-oil based, 144
for furniture, 142
German experience with,
  134
stability studies for, 135
study of variables in polyester systems, 138
"urethane oils," 143
"Vulcaprene A," 116
wire, 137, 139

Desmodurs, 29
  adhesives used in, 125, 126
  composition of, 8
  use in coatings, 136
Desmophens, 29
  adhesives used in, 125, 126
  composition of, 7
  use in coatings, 136
Diisocyanates
  American capacity, 10
  American trade names, table
    of, 13
  first commercial use in
    America, 5
  handling of, 15, 163-166
  relative activities of, 21, 22,
    23, 161
Dimer acids, 99
  foams from, 100

Diphenyl methane, 4,4'-diiso-
cyanate
relative activity of, 22
trade names for, 13
use in adhesives, 128, 129,
133
Du Pont, E. I., 4, 5, 6, 9, 10,
13, 57, 58, 116

Fibers. *See* "Perlon U."
cellulose phenyl thioure-
thane, 152
Finishes, textile, 155
Foams
flexible, 75-105
aging of, 100
applications of, 75, 93,
102
characteristics of, 81
comparison of various
bases for, 103
dyeing of, 93
foaming of, 80
mechanical means for,
83
handling of, 90
polyester formulations, 80,
83
polyether, 79, 104
stress-strain curves for,
75, 99
rigid, 29-54. *See also* Mul-
topren, Goodyear Air-
craft, and Lockheed
application of, 42
contrasted to semi-rigid
foams, 55, 56
electrical characteristics
of, 48
factors affecting density
and structure of, 36

foamed-in-place, 41
physical characteristics of,
48, 51
for slab stock, 53
water-density relationship
of, 40
semi-rigid, 55-74
adhesion of, 66
applications of, 68
contrasted to rigid foams,
definition of, 55, 56
effect of solvents on, 67
foaming technique for, 68
formulations, 57
as packaging material, 71
physical characteristics of,
59
self-snuffing property, 67
sound absorption of, 67,
68
spraying of, 67
thermal characteristics of,
65, 66
water absorption of, 66

"Gerbstoff H," 160
Goodyear Aircraft Corp., 38
Air Force development contract, 8, 31
rigid foam formulation and
technique, **8, 31**
Goodyear Tire & Rubber Co.,
114

Handling of diisocyanates, 15,
163-166
Hentschel, 5, 11
Hindered isocyanates (isocyanate generators), 26
as cross-linking agents for
textiles, 154

Hindered isocyanates (*cont'd*)
  history of, 26
  preparation of, 27
  use in coatings, 137, 142
Hoffman, 5
"Hylene TU," formula for, 13

"Igamid U," 6
Isocyanates
  history of preparation, 5
  irritating effect of, 136, 163-165
  linkage, 4
  reaction rates, 25, 26
  reaction, with active hydrogen, 16
    with amines, 17
    with carboxylic acid, 23, 24
    with hydroxyl, 17
    with urea, 17
    with urethane, 17
    with water, 24, 25
  review article on, 11

Kline, G. M., 4

Lockheed Aircraft Corporation, 38
  foam system, 34
    history of, 8, 10
  patents, 34

Methylene bis-(4-phenyl isocyanate). *See* Diphenylmethane-4,4'-diisocyanate
Mobay Chemical Co., 9, 10, 77, 78, 79, 83, 112, 135, 138

Mold release, 42, 43
Moltopren, 32
  compressive strength of, 30
  definition of, 29
  preparation of, 29
Monsanto Chemical Co., 9

National Aniline Corp., 10, 58, 133, 145, 159

Orchin, M., 144

"Perlon U," 6, 28, 147
  characteristics of, 150, 151
  effect of composition on, 149
  handling of, 150
  improvement of, 151
  preparation of, 148
    alternate method, 150, 151
Phenyl urethane formulation, effect of catalyst on, 20
Pinten, 107
Polyaryl polyisocyanate (PAPI), use in adhesive field, 127
Polyethers, 118
  types of, 104
"Polystal," 125
Polyurethane
  definition of 1, 3, 4
  history of, 5
  linear, 3, 6
Potting
  castor-oil base for, 157
  foam, 47
    advantages of, 51
  operation, 50, 51
  solid, 157

Prepolymers
castor-oil, 57
effect of water on, 25
potential, 81
quasi, 54, 74

Radome, 8, 31, 48
preparation of, 42
Reilly, C. B., 144
Rubber (urethane), 106-123
advantages and disadvantages of, 106
applications, 106

Saunders, J. H. and Slocombe, R. J., 11
Schlack, 107
Structural core applications, 50

Tanning, use of low active diisocyanate for, 160
"Teracol," 79
Toluene diisocyanates, 29, 31
freezing point-composition graph, 15
German names, 7
preparation, industrial, 11
of various isomer ratios, 14
relative activities of, 21, 22, 23
trade names for, 8

Urethane
ethyl, 1, 2
formation of, 17
effect of various catalysts on, 19, 20
inhibitors, 18, 20
via chlorocarbonic acid esters, 27, 28
reaction with isocyanate, 18
"Urethane oils," 143

"Vulcaprene A," 116
as coating material, 116, 117
blends, 117
preparation of, 116
"Vulcollan," 107, 116, 118
advantages and disadvantages of, 111, 112, 114
applications of, 111
effect of dibasic acids on, 108, 109
effect of diisocyanate on, 110
preparation of, 108
cross-linking agents used in, 111
"Vulkollan" (German), 124
"Vulkollans," 112, 116
applications of, 112, 113

Wöhler, 1
Wurtz, 5